FOLK-TALES
FROM GREECE
II

to my sister Artemis
M.S.

FOLK-TALES
FROM GREECE
II

Retold by Menelaos Stephanides
Illustrated by Photini Stephanidi

Translation
Bruce Walter

ଓ

SIGMA

FOLK-TALES FROM GREECE: II

First edition 2002, second run 2005
Printed in Greece by "Fotolio-Typicon", bound by G. Betsoris
Copyright© 2002: Sigma Publications

SIGMA PUBLICATIONS
20, Mavromihali Street, GR-106 80 Athens
tel. +30 210 3607667, fax +30 210 3638941
www.sigmabooks.gr   e-mail: sigma@sigmabooks.gr

ISBN: 960-425-083-3

CONTENTS

Three Pieces of Advice

There was once a poor man called Antonis. He lived in a small village with his wife and only child, a boy about ten years of age. So terrible was their poverty, however, that he decided to leave home and go in search of work.

"This is no life we're leading here," he told his wife. "I'll go and work in the city to make some money, and when I come back we can live in comfort."

"Go, then, but don't forget us," his wife replied – and the very next day, she and their son bade him farewell with tears in their eyes.

Antonis went to the city, but there was no work to be had. After many days, he found a job as servant to a nobleman – but his master was very mean.

"I'll pay you when your time is up, so you don't squander all your wages," he announced. And the poor man had no choice but to accept.

Antonis worked hard and well. Though he was never given any money, he told himself to be patient. Ten whole years went by like this, till in the end he decided to ask for his wages and leave.

Now his master had to decide what to pay him, and he told himself:

"A hundred pounds is too much by far. If I give him fifty, that's still a lot. Let's give him twenty, say. But has he really earned his keep? I'll give him ten instead." In the end he took out not ten pounds, but five – and even then he only gave him three of them.

"Is that all?" poor Antonis gasped.

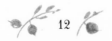

"That's all your work is worth," the nobleman replied. "Still, if you think it's not enough, stay on for another ten years and I'll give you three pounds more."

But the sum was so small, and the years so long, that Antonis took the money with a sigh and left.

On the road home, he met an old man with a long white beard.

"If you give me a pound, I'll give you a good piece of advice," the old man said. Antonis thought for a while then told himself:

"Well, I'm poor with three pounds and not much poorer with two." So he gave one of his pounds to the old man, who told him:

> *"Don't ask if it isn't your concern!*
> *That's the first thing you must learn."*

This is my first piece of advice to you. And if you want another, which is even better than the first, just

give me another pound."

"I'm poor with two pounds and not much poorer with one," thought Antonis, and he gave the old man a second coin.

"Just keep to your way
And don't be led astray."

That's my second piece of advice," the old man told him. But if you want a third, which will help you even more than the second, give me one more pound."

"Well, I'm poor with one pound and just the same with nothing," said Antonis again. And he gave the old man his last gold coin.

"If you get angry in the night,
Don't act on it until first light."

the old man told him. "That is my final piece of advice to you."

As he went on his way, poor Antonis wondered:

15

"Did I do the right thing or not? Ah well, I was poor with three pounds, and with nothing in my pocket, what's the difference?" And on he walked.

A little further down the road he came upon a black man, ten feet tall, who was doing something very odd indeed. He was gluing gold sovereigns onto the leaves of a lemon tree!

Antonis stopped short in surprise. He was about to ask him why he was performing this strange task when he remembered the old man's first piece of advice:

> *'Don't ask if it isn't your concern*
> *That's the first thing you must learn.'*

And so he just bade the black man good day and continued on his way.

"Hey! Where are you going?" the black man shouted. "Come back and fill your pockets with gold sovereigns. And do you know why I'm letting you have them? A hundred years I've been sticking these coins on the tree, and nobody ever passes by without stopping to ask me why. Here's what happened to the last one who passed this way – it wasn't long ago. A little fellow he was, and of course he stopped to ask me why I was sticking sovereigns on the lemon tree.

'What did you say?' I asked.

'Why are you gluing sovereigns on the leaves?' he repeated.

'I can't hear,' I replied. 'Speak in my other ear.'

'Why are you sticking gold coins on the tree?'

'I can't hear! Speak louder!' I told him – just joking, of course. Then he shouted out his question once again – so loud that it made him hoarse.

'Louder!' I repeated.

So he shouted, I shouted, I lost my temper, and then I gave him a slap on the face with this great paw of mine, which left him stone deaf in one ear. Then I gave him another with the other hand, which left him deaf as a post in the other ear as well. He staggered off with his head spinning. No more questions about sovereigns from him! To cut a long story short, that's more or less what's happened to every nosy traveller who passes by. I've sent the lot of them packing – some lamed, some blinded, some as mad as hatters. You're the only one who didn't ask me a single question – just wished me good day and continued on your way. So take as many sovereigns as you like, for you deserve them."

Delighted, Antonis crammed his pockets with as many gold coins as they would hold, thanked the black man and continued on his journey home.

"A pound for that piece of advice was money well spent," he told himself. "Some came healthy and left crippled, others came with sharp ears and left stone deaf, some were driven mad – but I came poor and left rich!"

A little further down the road he met some travellers who were going the same way. They exchanged greetings and all went on together.

Soon they came to a crossroads where there was a sign with an arrow, pointing to a tavern.

"Let's go and have a drink," said one of the travellers.

"Why not?" the others all agreed.

The words 'why not' were on the tip of Antonis's tongue, too, when he remembered the second piece of advice:

Just keep to your way
And don't be led astray.'

So instead of going with the others he said, "I'll sit here and wait for you." And with these words he seated himself beneath a tree and, tired from his long walk, soon fell asleep.

All of a sudden, he was woken up by a man who came staggering towards him with his clothes all burned and flopped down on the grass beside the tree.

"What a disaster!" groaned the stranger.

"Disaster? What disaster?" asked Antonis in surprise.

"What," cried the stranger, "didn't you see anything? Didn't you hear it?"

"I was fast asleep – and you've just woken me up," replied Antonis rather crossly.

"Well," continued the stranger, "this is how I lost everything I have in the world. I was just about to lock my tavern up and go off home, when a group of travellers arrived. How was I to know what would happen next? They seemed ordinary enough folks to me. They asked for brandy and I served it with roast almonds. They began to eat and drink – especially to drink!

'More brandy!' they demanded – and I brought it to them.

'More – and more!' they shouted.

What else could I do? I gave them what they asked for. They got drunk as lords! Suddenly, one of them pulled a pistol from his belt and 'bang!' a shot went through the ceiling. Then another drew his weapon and 'boom!' a bullet smashed into a barrel of brandy. Then they all began shooting, 'bang! boom! bang!' They made matchwood of the barrels. The tavern was ankle-deep in ouzo, wine and brandy. I stood there tearing my hair while they danced a drunken reel in the puddles of spilled drink.

'You villains! You've ruined me!' I cried.

'Let us alone! We are going to have a ball tonight!' laughed one of them – and took aim at a barrel filled with paraffin. That was that. The whole tavern was wrapped in flames before I knew what was happening. Luckily, I was standing in the doorway and was able to dive for safety, or I would have been burned alive like all the others. Well, they got what they asked for – but what about me? Was it my fault that everything I possess has gone up in a cloud of smoke? Can you tell me that?"

What could Antonis say? He sat there openmouthed and thought, 'I got off lightly! A pound is all that piece of advice cost me. The old man was right when he said that the second was worth much more than the first.'

After many days of walking, Antonis eventually reached home. Night had fallen by the time he arrived, and in the darkness his wife did not even recognize him.

'And perhaps it would be better not to tell her who I am just yet,' thought Antonis. 'I've been away so many years it would be wiser to wait and find out what's been going on here in my absence.'

So he told her, "I'm just passing through. Make up a bed for me somewhere, would you?" And he gave her two gold sovereigns for her pains.

"I'm sorry," his wife replied, "but I can't let you into the house. You can sleep down in the store room, though — and as for money, in these parts we don't accept it for such small services." Then she gave him back the two gold coins, brought him a bowl of steaming soup and two thick blankets and went inside the house again, locking the door behind her.

A few moments later, Antonis made out through the darkness the tall figure of a man going upstairs to the house. The blood rushed to his head.

"The faithless creature!" he cried in a rage. "She's forgotten me and married someone else, while I was slaving away for her, far off in the city. I'll kill her! No, I'll kill them both!" He drew his pistol from his belt and was about to charge upstairs when he remembered the old man's third piece of advice:

> *'When you get angry in the night,*
> *Don't act on it until first light.'*

He stood there hesitating, but he was still boiling with rage. "No! Now! Why in the morning? It's the same thing, isn't it?" But then he thought better of it and said, "Leave it for tomorrow. I paid a pound for that piece of advice, and it would be a pity to let it go to waste."

Soon afterwards he fell into a troubled sleep – but not for long. Somehow he found himself on his feet again, crying out, "I'll shoot them both, the villains!" But even as the words left his mouth, he remembered that the old man had told him this third and final word of advice was worth even more than the second, so he decided after all that he would wait till morning came before he killed the guilty couple.

In his troubled state of mind, it was a long time before Antonis got back to sleep, and when he awoke he could already hear morning footsteps overhead. His blood boiled once again but he told himself,

"Let God punish them for their guilty deeds, not

me," and he threw open the door, intending to quit the house once and for all. At that very moment the door above him opened too and he heard a man's voice saying, "Good-bye, mother. I won't be late to-night."

When Antonis heard this, he banged his fist against his forehead in dismay.

"My God!" he cried. "I must have been out of my mind! I would have killed my own son and his mother!"

He rushed upstairs and threw his arms around them both. They hugged and kissed and wept with joy. Then Antonis took them into the house, emptied his loaded pockets of the sovereigns and spread them out upon the table.

"This gold is precious enough, to be sure," he told them, "but more precious still is the advice that I was given. An old man told me three things, but the best by far was his third piece of advice:

'*If you get angry in the night,*
Don't act on it until first light.'

And with these words he hugged and kissed them once again. Antonis was home at last, and they all lived happily ever after.

The Lettuce Leaf

nce upon a time there lived a harmless fat donkey, a cunning fox and a wolf who was as stupid as he was wicked.

One day, the donkey was grazing all alone in a green meadow on the edge of the forest. Nearby, amongst the trees, the fox was lurking. Suddenly she caught sight of the donkey and told herself,

'I'll go to find the wolf – and if we put our heads together, then with my cunning and his strength, it'll be curtains for the donkey. We'll get him alone somewhere and gobble him all up.'

Hardly had she set out when who should appear

but the wolf.

"Ah, Mr Wolf, I was just coming to find you!" cried the fox. "Do you see that donkey grazing over there? Now there's a sight to make your mouth water!"

"Ho, ho, ho!" said the wolf when he spotted the donkey. "How well-fed and fat he is! Come on, Mrs Fox, think of some way we can catch him. You've got a sharp mind."

"Of course I have," she retorted, "and I've got a clever idea all ready and waiting. You didn't think I was going to wait for you to come up with a plan, did you?"

"Tell me quickly, then, Mrs Fox!" pleaded the wolf. "Don't keep me in suspense!"

"Listen," the fox told him. "You go and find a boat and pretend that you're a fisherman. Meanwhile, I'll make friends with the donkey and bring him to you. As for the rest, just leave it all to me."

"I know I can count on you, Mrs Fox," replied the

wolf. "This will be a meal to remember, that's for sure!" And off he went in search of a boat.

The cunning fox left the trees and sidled over to the donkey. When she got up to him she said, ever so politely,

"Good morning to you, Mr Donkey! It's been such a long time since I saw you, I was beginning to wonder how you were. There are so many things I have to tell you! Why don't you come along with me for a little boat trip, and then we can have a nice long chat together. I've got a good friend who's a fisherman, and he can take us out."

The donkey liked the idea of a little outing, and so the two of them set off for the seaside. They found the wolf waiting, with the boat drawn up on the sand, and after they had pushed it into the water, all three got on board. Taking turns at the oars, they rowed the boat a good way from the shore. And then the cunning fox remarked,

"You see that little cloud above the mountain? I don't like the look of it at all. I'm afraid a storm may blow up. I don't believe that we're in fear of drowning, but all the same, it might be wiser for us to make our confessions, just in case. Let's confess our sins and earn forgiveness – we've nothing to lose by it."

"Nothing to lose at all," agreed the wolf.

"No, nothing whatsoever," said the donkey.

"Come on then, Mr Wolf – hear my confession," said the fox.

"You mean you have committed sins, then, Mrs Fox?"

"I've only made off with a hen or two, wrung the necks of a few ducks and gobbled up a rabbit now and then."

"Oh, that's nothing," laughed the wolf. "They're miserable creatures anyway. You did quite right to eat them. No, Mrs Fox, you don't seem to have committed any sins. Now you confess me."

"Why, do you have sins upon your conscience, Mr Wolf?"

"That's just what I'm wondering myself. Of course, I've eaten a few cows, I've stripped the bones off more than a few sheep, I've stolen nanny goats upon occasion, I've ...."

He was going to say, 'I've had a donkey for my dinner more than once', but at the last moment, stupid though he was, he remembered who was in the boat with them and held his tongue.

"And they are all you've eaten?" asked the fox. "Why, miserable creatures, every one. You had every right to eat them. No, you've not committed any sins."

Then she turned to the donkey and said,

"Now it's your turn, Mr Donkey. Tell us your sins, please – every single one of them."

"Well, there is one sin that's been nagging at my conscience for a long time now," the donkey admitted, hanging his head in shame.

"Tell us, tell us, Mr Donkey!" cried the other two, the saliva dripping from their jaws.

"I will, then," said the donkey. "Once my master loaded me with two heavy baskets of lettuces. It was a very hot day and I was terribly hungry and thirsty. A lovely cool, tender lettuce leaf was hanging over the edge of one of the baskets and I really fancied it. So when my master wasn't looking, I turned my head around and ate it."

"You did what?" cried out the fox and wolf in horror.

"I ate the lettuce leaf."

"Just ate the lettuce leaf, you say?
No oil? No vinegar? – No way!
We're lucky that we're still afloat!
God's going to sink us and the boat!"

"Yes," confessed the donkey, "I ate it. That is my great sin."

It did not take the fox and the wolf very long to come to their decision.

"You have committed a great sin indeed – and we must eat you," they announced solemnly.

"Whaaat?" cried the donkey, and his great dark eyes grew larger still.

"We must eat you," the fox repeated. "We can't afford to have a sinner like you on board with us. We shall all be drowned because of you. There's no escape for us unless we eat you."

To which the wolf added,

"Yes, we're sure to drown. There's no saving us with such a wicked fellow in the boat. We must gobble him up as fast as we can, Mrs Fox. Look! That cloud over the mountain is getting bigger. I can see it with my own eyes!"

"It is, it is – bigger by the minute!" the fox agreed, and she put on a frightened look to convince the donkey.

Now Mr Donkey may have been a harmless fellow, but he was no fool. He knew by now exactly what the wicked pair were up to, and it did not take him long to see how he could get himself out of the dangerous situation he was in. He acted just as if he were the miserable sinner that they claimed he was, and in a pitiful voice he begged,

"All right, all right. Please don't go on at me like that. Eat me if you must, for I know I don't deserve to live. But let me beg one last small favour of you. My father sent me a letter just before he died, and I would like you to read it to me, so I can make the journey into the next world in peace. Something about sheep and goats I think it says."

The wolf sprang up at once.

"What sheep? What goats?" he asked, his mouth watering.

"If I knew that, why would I ask you to read the letter?" said the donkey.

"And where is this letter?" asked the wolf impatiently.

"Here, on my hoof," the donkey said, and lifted his hind leg. "Come over here, Mr Wolf, and read me what my father wrote – and after that you can eat me."

The stupid wolf bent down to read the writing. "Don't!" shouted the cunning fox. But before he realised what she was saying the donkey gave him a hefty kick right on his muzzle and overboard went Mr Wolf! Terrified that she would get the next kick, the fox jumped in the water too – and so the wicked partners who had tried to eat poor Mr Donkey were both drowned in the sea.

The Twelve Months

nce upon a time there lived a good, kind woman but she was so poor that life was a terrible struggle for her. Her husband had died and left her with five fatherless children. How was she to bring them up and send them off into the world with a good start? She was the kindest mother there could be, but kindness alone was not enough to feed five hungry mouths.

Close to her humble home stood a great mansion and in it lived a rich lady with her husband and their children. Once a week the poor woman went to this rich neighbour's house and made bread for her. But the rich lady was both mean and evil and gave her nothing for her pains. Yet the poor woman went willingly to do the work, for when she had finished kneading all the dough she would go home with her arms all white with flour, and that is how she fed her children. You see, she would wash the flour off in a saucepan of clean water and place it on the fire to boil. In this way she would make a kind of thin gruel and feed it to her orphaned children, who had nothing else to eat, poor things. All the other days of the week they lived with empty stomachs, but they would wait patiently for their kind mother to go and make their neighbours' bread and come home with her arms all white with flour.

You would have thought her children would be thin and pale, growing up so poor and hungry. Instead, they were rosy-cheeked and sturdy. Not only that, but they always had a smile on their lips and were radiant with grace and beauty. For they were growing up warmed by their mother's love and the kindness of her heart.

It was not the same with their wicked neighbour's children. For they were spoiled and horrible and quarrelled bitterly from dawn to dusk. This made their faces cross and ugly, and because they always turned their noses up at the food she set before them they were paler and skinnier by far than the poor woman's children.

"Why should that creature's children be so happy and good-looking?" the rich lady asked herself, "and why should mine be so pasty-faced and scowling? Ah! Now I understand what is to blame. It's all her fault. She never washes the flour off her arms before she leaves my house and that way she manages to steal my darlings' health away. Well, she won't get away with it next time!"

And so, when the poor woman came to make the bread again, she would not let her leave for home until she had washed every speck of flour from both her arms.

The unlucky woman set off for her poor cottage weeping in despair, and when her children saw her coming through the door with empty hands, they burst out crying as well. Their mother turned to wipe away her tears, and putting a brave smile on her face she told them,

"Try to sleep, my little ones, and I shall go to find the good water-fairy and tell her we are hungry. She is kind and tender-hearted and loves good children and she will give me a great big loaf of bread to bring home so that all of us can eat."

Steeling her heart, the unfortunate woman turned and left the house at once, unable to bear the sight of her starving children.

She made her way up into the wild mountains. On and on she trudged until, in a deserted spot, she spied a castle. She walked up to its gates, went in,

and there, in a great high-ceilinged chamber, were sitting twelve young men.

Three of them had their shirts unbuttoned and held branches all in bloom. Three others were bare from the waist up and carried sheaves of ripe, golden corn. Three more were holding bunches of black grapes and the last three were wrapped from head to foot in thick, warm furs.

As soon as the young men saw the stranger, they rose to welcome her. They found a seat for her, and when they saw that she was hungry they gave her food to eat. Only when her appetite was satisfied did they ask her how she came to be in these wild parts and stumble on their castle.

Then the poor woman told the young men of her troubles and looked into their faces, one by one. How good-hearted they all seemed! She knew she must have won their sympathy.

"Tell us, dear lady, do you like the months of

spring – March, April and May?" asked the three young men who held the sprays of blossom in their arms.

"All these months are beautiful, my lads," she answered, "for then the earth is carpeted with green and decked out with brightly-coloured flowers. The air smells sweet and the birds all sing for joy. We should be ungrateful if we did not love these months when the young shoots of our crops grow taller by the day and the fruit begins to take shape on the trees."

"How do you like the months of summer, then – June with its harvests, July and the heat of August?" asked the three young men whose brown chests were all bare.

"They are good months, too, my boys, all three of them. The hot days ripen the crops and the young beasts grow apace. The farmers reap their corn and winnow it, they pick the ripe fruit from the trees and are happy that their labour has been well rewarded."

"September, then, October and November? How do you fare when these three months come in?" asked the young men who held great bunches of ripe grapes. "How do you like the autumn time, dear lady?"

"The labourer longs for these three months as well," replied the poor woman. "One gathers in his grapes from off the vine, another picks his olives and presses golden oil from them, and everybody waits for these three months to come, for that is when the rains soften the soil, so that the farmer can plough and sow his fields. Who could not want these things, when all of us depend upon the earth to feed us?"

"And how do you feel about the winter months?" asked December, January and February. The last of these was lame, poor lad.

"We all get by quite happily, my boys. We need

these months no less than all the rest. It is a time for sitting round the fire and resting from the labours of the other seasons. It is a time when boys and girls enjoy their parents' company, for there is no work to keep them in the fields. In the winter months come Christmas and New Year, and many other festivals where folks feast and sing and dance. Yes, all the months are good, my lads. Each has its own delights and brings the changes men and women need so much. And what is most important, they give our lives a pattern we can follow. Alas, if only my husband were still with us! He was a good hard worker, and were he still alive, our children would not go hungry now."

The twelve young men, who were of course none other than the twelve months of the year, gave the poor woman a sympathetic look and decided they would give a present to her. One of them left the hall and came back carrying a jar with a wax seal.

"This is so your children won't go hungry," they all said, and one of them broke its seal.

And what did the poor woman see? Why, the jar was full of golden sovereigns! She hugged each one of them in turn, sobbing out her thanks, then set off down the mountainside weeping with joy.

When she got back to town, the first thing she did was to buy food for her hungry children, and then she hurried home to tell them the good news. Next she bought some good warm clothes for them and treated herself to a dress she need not be ashamed to wear. Before long, the whole house was transformed and the bitter years of hunger were only a bad memory.

The rich woman was puzzled when she saw these changes. She was eaten up by jealousy and curiosity – so much so that she went and asked her good neighbour where all these things had come from. Of course, the kindly soul told her who had helped her in her need and where the young men could be found.

Without wasting a moment, the rich woman dressed herself in rags and set off for the rugged mountains. She found the castle, and the twelve young men invited her inside.

They sat her down to eat, but she just eyed the food and sniffed at it, but did not eat a single mouthful.

"I found a crust of dry bread by the wayside," she excused herself, "and now I've eaten that, it's taken all my appetite away."

The young men were no fools. They knew the real reason why she was not hungry.

"How do you manage, down there in the town?" asked one of them.

"Terribly, terribly," she answered. "Things could not be worse."

"But surely, it's not bad all year long. Which is the best month?"

"The best? Why don't you ask me which of them is worst! All through the summer months we can't breathe, it's so hot. Then come September, October and November and we can't set foot outside the door with all that rain – not to mention the back-breaking work that autumn brings. It's sheer misery, I tell you. Then come December, January and that accursed February with one leg three days shorter than the other (February winced at that cruel remark!), and between the three of them they keep us all shut up inside with their bitter north winds and their snow. And then the spring months come at last, when we've almost given up hope of seeing a fine day again. But what do we get instead? As soon as March comes in, the weather turns cold and wet again, and endless work on top of it. No, curse the spring, I say – and all the other months, too, my boys. One ends and another one begins, but we never see good come of it, not even for the rich. As for we poor folks, why, don't even ask. Come on, though, lads, help a poor woman who's down on her luck and then perhaps I shall be able to forget the misfortunes that the cursed months have loaded on me."

The young men made no answer to the rich woman's wicked words. They just gave a nod to February, who went limping off and came back with a jar just like the first.

"This is for you," they told her. "Only be careful not to open it on your way home, in case anyone should see you. Don't break the seal until you're safe at home – and then only with the doors and windows tightly shut."

"I know, I know," answered the rich woman impatiently. "I'm not fool enough to go opening it in front of others. I shall be all alone, don't worry."

Trembling with eagerness, she snatched the pitcher and ran out of the castle without even stopping to say 'thank you'. She hurried all the way home,

rushed into her room and quickly locked the doors and bolted all the windows so she could feast her eyes upon the treasure all alone. But the moment she broke the wax that sealed the jar she gave a piercing shriek and fell senseless to the floor – for it was not sovereigns that filled the jar, but a nest of writhing snakes!

The Swot

nce upon a time, there lived a king and queen who had three sons. The king was very fond of the two older ones, who strutted around in splendid golden uniforms and were such skilled swordsmen and good riders that they were always champions in tournaments and leaders of parades. He was so proud of them that he thanked God daily for giving him such sons to rule the kingdom when his time was done.

But for his youngest son he felt no love at all, although the young man had a heart of gold. You see, he did not care about fine clothes and golden-hilted swords and besides, he was short and slightly-built while the others were as tall as houses. Yet what he lacked in height he more than made up by his knowledge. He loved to study and was forever buried in his room, which was filled with books right up to the ceiling. There he would sit, bent over his books and 'swotting' as his brothers rudely called it, when really he was learning all the wisdom of the world. The other two might love their hunting and even kill wild boars, but he would never even hurt a fly. 'Swot by nature and Swot by name', his brothers used to jeer, till in the end his real name, which was Demos, had almost been forgotten. "Swot" was the only name they called him now, and both the king and his two brothers considered him unfit for any deed which required strength and daring.

Now luckily the queen adored young Swot as much as all the others despised him. She was happy to see him wrapped up in his studies, and gave him

all the money he needed to go on buying books and adding to his store of knowledge. Not a volume came onto the market but he would buy it before the ink had dried.

One book that came into his hands was called 'The Kingdom with the Castle of the Three Maidens', and it impressed him greatly. Realising from the very first page that he had a lot to learn from it, he threw himself into his reading. His studies were rewarded, for from this book he learned things which astonished him. It appeared that in a distant corner of the world there lay a kingdom whose people lived in peace and happiness. Words such as hatred, revenge, greed, trickery and crime were unknown in those parts, and everyone lived on happily into deep old age, for they had learned all nature's store of remedies and whoever had the mischance to fall ill was very soon made well again. Naturally enough, they all loved their worthy king and his good queen, but they kept a special place in their hearts for the three princesses, maidens lovelier than human eyes had ever seen before.

Yet although the people there had almost all that they could wish for, there was one great problem that beset them. Quite without warning, sometimes once a year, sometimes every two, but occasionally even twice within twelve months, a sudden sleep would fall upon them all, turning them to statues where they stood. Whoever happened to be walking down the street, let's say, would be frozen there with one leg poised to take another step. And this sleep always lasted three months to the day, not a moment more or less. Although these people had found remedies for every illness known to man, they could find no cure for this mysterious sleeping sickness.

It seems the curse had fallen on them some hundred years before. At that time three witches had come into the kingdom, and as the folk in those parts feared such creatures, they told them they had no need of their services and offered them no hospitality. They simply made it clear that all they wanted them to do was to go and peddle their wares elsewhere.

On hearing this, the angry witches cast a spell on them. And the strangest thing of all, as we have seen, was that every one of them was fixed in sleep in exactly the position he had been in when the spell was cast, and did not move from it until three months had passed. The worst part was that the curse kept coming back and no one had yet found a way of stopping it. The only clue was that a wise old man had said, as he lay dying, that the evil would be lifted from them only if love could make six roses fall to earth after a six-month journey. But what these words meant nobody could rightly explain, and countless experiments with roses and long marches proved in vain.

This and much else young Swot discovered by reading of the kingdom with the castle of the three maidens, and he studied everything about it he could lay his hands on. It was no small thing to learn that somewhere there was a world of peace and love, and what is more that all illness could be cured there. Yet why should they have the problem of their months' long sleep? And this was not the only question he asked himself. Why should the royal palace be called the castle of the three maidens, and what kind of maidens could they be? Was the book exaggerating when it claimed that human eyes had never seen such lovely girls before? Ah, how he longed to go and see it all, especially the three princesses. But this kingdom lay a six-month march away – at least, that's what the book said – and cut off from the outside world by fearsome obstacles, so such a journey was impossible. And yet, the very evening he had been thinking all these things, he found himself in that far country the moment that sleep closed his eyes. He admired everything he saw around him, but when his eyes fell on the king's three daughters his mouth fell open in amazement, for they were even lovelier than he had imagined them. The youngest was the fairest of them all. It was love at first sight. Poor Swot was so smitten that when he woke and found her gone you would have wept to see him. If only the dream could come true and he could see the beautiful princess once again! But such a miracle was more than anyone dare hope for. All the books said so, and our love-stricken young prince was plunged into despair.

For all his longing, he could not bring himself to make the perilous journey. However, when his father suddenly fell ill and needed medicine only to be found in that far-off land, his mind was made up for him. What had seemed impossible till now must be achieved at all costs, though it proved a terrifying

ordeal which put his life in danger more than once. Yet in the end, of course, everything turned out happily, as it always does in fairy tales.

No, don't smile – just listen to what happened:

One day, Swot's father's eyes began to hurt. The most famous doctors in the realm were called to his side, then others were summoned from the neighbouring kingdoms, but nothing could be done. The king's condition worsened by the day, till in the end he was completely blind.

Everyone in the palace was terribly upset, but once they saw there was nothing to be done they resigned themselves to the unhappy situation. Everyone, that is, except young Swot, who once more buried himself in the book about the kingdom of the three maidens; the difference being that now he was not reading about the princesses, not even the youngest and most beautiful, but feverishly turning over the pages devoted to medicines and curing illnesses. Finally he found what he was looking for. It seemed that in the courtyard of the palace there was a lemon tree growing in a special kind of earth. If you made mud from this and smeared it on a blind man's eyes, he would regain his sight immediately. Now Swot's mind was made up for him. He would journey to that distant kingdom in the hope he might bring back the magic soil and meet the maiden of his dreams as well. He went and told his mother everything – not only about the magic cure but about his great love, too.

"You'll never make it, son!" the queen cried out. "Why wander off into the unknown to meet a certain death? We have all learned to live with the misfortune that befell your father, and as for the princess, why, when the time comes we'll marry you to the loveliest maiden in our kingdom."

But Swot was not to be dissuaded. Little by little he brought his mother round and in the end she went and told the king about the magic earth, admitting how far away it lay, but not revealing that the journey there would be well-nigh impossible.

"Send Swot to bring the magic earth?" the king replied. "Out of the question! Our two eldest sons must go instead. Besides," he added, "you said yourself how far away this kingdom lies. Who knows how many obstacles lie in the way? The youngster would give up, for sure. Why send the little runt when we have two such splendid sons?"

When Swot learned what his father had decided, he begged his mother once again to let him go instead.

"My brothers will never find the place," he told her, "so what sort of earth can you expect them to bring back?"

"I know, my son," replied the queen. "Those two will give up the search at the first difficulty they encounter. That's why I have no fears for them; it's you I'm worried about."

In the meantime, the king summoned his two favourite sons and told them to go in search of the magic earth. He ordered each of them to be provided with a troop of fifty soldiers and, having filled their pockets with gold crowns and given them rich gifts for the ruler of that distant land, he sent the two groups galloping off on horseback. In spite of this, Swot still kept pestering his mother who, knowing that the king would never listen to her, decided to put the twelve royal counsellors in the picture. So in the end it was they who persuaded the king that the only way to get his eyesight back was to send Swot on the journey, too. After all, he was the one who had done all the studying needed to find the way to the distant kingdom.

With a heavy heart, the king at last agreed to let his youngest son, the 'runt of the family' as he called him, go on the search as well.

"Give him a purse with a few gold crowns in it,

and good luck to him," he said reluctantly. And so young Swot, who had only been waiting for the word, set off immediately, determined to come back with the magic earth or die in the attempt. But he also had a hidden longing to see the lovely princess of his dreams again. Who knows, if fortune smiled on him she might return his love and come back with him to his father's kingdom.

On the way, he asked everyone he met if they had seen his brothers passing by, and in the end he found them.

"Where are you off to?" they asked him in surprise.

"The same place you are going," he replied.

"If father's waiting on you to get his eyesight back, then heaven help him! Courage and daring are what's needed here, not little bookworms like yourself," said the eldest brother scornfully.

"I'll do my best," retorted Swot. "Why, does it

bother you?"

"Have a go, then – but not along with us. You take your own road."

"No, let him come," broke in the second brother. "You never know, he could be useful to us. Perhaps he really is the only one who knows where this mysterious kingdom is, and how to find the magic earth."

"I suppose you're right," the eldest one admitted. "Come along, then."

They had been travelling for ninety days when they reached a spot where the road split into three, and each of its three branches was grassy and untrodden. It was clear they would have to make some kind of choice.

"What do your books say now?" enquired the eldest in a jeering tone.

"Listen, brothers," said young Swot, "I've seen these three roads in a book of mine, and they all lead to the kingdom that we want to reach. But there are such fearsome obstacles on each of them that no traveller has ever dared to try. The road on the right goes through a region swept by whirlwinds that will suck both horse and rider a hundred feet into the air. If you are lucky enough to stay in the saddle, you may get through, but if you don't, you're doomed. The middle road crosses a plain which belches fire and smoke. Twenty-four hours on horseback it'll take us to get through, if we're not burnt to cinders long before."

"Let's hear about the third road, then," the eldest brother demanded.

"That one is the road of no return."

"And if we take it, we're finished either way?" the second asked.

"That's what the books say," Swot replied. "So why don't you choose one road each, and whichever one is left I'll take myself."

"Look here, young Swot," replied the eldest brother, "I don't like the sound of this one little bit. Are you quite sure there isn't a safer road to this kingdom of yours?"

"There's no other road shown on the maps," Swot told him. "And if there is, not even the wise men who drew them could have known about it, so what else can we do?"

They hummed and hahed till in the end the eldest took the right-hand road, the middle brother took the middle road and poor Swot was left with the road of no return. Before they parted, he had a bright idea:

"So we shall know if any of the others managed to get back, let's each of us leave a ring under this stone. Whenever one of us passes by this way again he can put his ring back on, and that will be a sign to whoever follows after."

And so, having placed their rings beneath the

stone, each brother went his separate way. The elder
two took all their followers and horses with them,
while the youngest set off all alone.

When the eldest brother had been riding twenty
days, he reached the place where the great whirlwinds blew, and when he saw everything swirling
all around him, and even whole trees being sucked
into the sky, his courage deserted him and he turned
back. Returning to the spot where they had left their
rings, he took his own, then, angry and disappointed,
made his way to the nearest town to await his brothers' return.

As for the second brother, he had been riding for
a month when he saw the smoke and fire of the
burning plain. He went on hesitantly, but as soon
as the first sparks singed his skin he lost his nerve
as well and turned his horse around. Beside himself
with rage, he returned and lifted up the stone. When
he saw that his elder brother's ring was no longer in

its place he realised that he, too, must have given up and so he rode off to the nearby town, where he found him at an inn.

Shamed by their failure, they did not know what to do next.

"Let's wait and see if Swot returns," the middle brother suggested.

"But if he comes back with the magic earth, we'll look a proper pair of cowards," the other pointed out. "How can we go back to father with empty hands, when he'll have the medicine in his?"

"First let's wait and see if he does come back – not that he will– and if he brings the earth –which he won't– then we'll see what we shall do," was the middle brother's answer.

But let us leave the sorry pair to wallow in their misery and return to see how their young brother was getting on. Now, from his reading, Swot knew all too well the terrors of the road he trod. Nobody had ever reached the other end alive. For above the road there loomed a tower where forty fearsome dragons lived together with a dragoness, their mother. If any traveller reached that point he could neither go on nor return, for the dragons would seize him in an instant and serve him up for dinner. But if we suppose that someone did somehow manage to slip by unnoticed and continue down the road, he would soon come to a second tower where another forty dragons lived. These also had a mother, and they would gobble him without even spitting up a fingernail. Yet even if he escaped their clutches, which was quite impossible, a little further on his way he would come to yet another tower, with yet another forty dragons and yet another fearsome mother. These were the most savage of them all, and there would be no hope of getting past alive. However, just for the sake of argument, let us suppose that by some miracle a traveller managed to escape the clutches of all three nests of dragons, what then? Why, then he would fall straight into the yawning jaws of a monster so huge that it blocked the whole road with its body, from the mountains to the sea.

Yet Swot was determined to let no obstacle prevent him from getting through, and so he walked on tirelessly for twenty days till the first tower came in sight.

"I must find some way of getting these dragons on my side," he told himself, "then perhaps with their help I can find some way of dealing with the monster." And that is exactly what he did, as we shall see.

Now in each tower the dragons were all brothers, and not only that but the dragons in the neighbouring towers were cousins, for their mothers the dragonesses were three sisters. These mother dragons had been born of the monster mentioned earlier. This nasty creature had the unpleasant habit of eating all the children it gave birth to, and these three only happened to escape because it made the mistake of leaving them to fatten up before it swallowed them. They soon realised why the monster was feeding them so well and took advantage of a moonless night to make good their escape. Swot knew all this from his reading, but had also learned another detail which would prove to be the most useful fact of all. He knew that in the first tower the dragons did not number forty, but only thirty-nine, since one of them had been lost when it was still a baby. So he decided to go to the dragon-mother and pull the wool over her eyes. Taking a stick of charcoal, he drew some lines around his eyes, then darkened his eyebrows and his cheeks to make himself look fierce. Not much of a disguise, you say? Ah, but it's a well-known fact that dragons are terribly short-sighted. Advancing very cautiously, he found the dragoness alone and suddenly stepped out in

front of her. She was just about to devour him alive
when he shouted:

"Don't! I am the son you lost all those years ago,
and now I have come back."

"How can you be my son when you're so small?"
the dragoness hissed. "Don't talk nonsense! You're
no dragon, even if you do look fierce."

"No, mother, I really am your son. I'm a dragon
just like you, but I fell among men when I was still a
baby, and they fed me so little and gave me so much
work to do that I never grew up to my proper size."

Now whether because young Swot had played
his role so well, or because the dragon-mother had
always longed to see her child again, or simply because she was rather stupid and, as we said, short-
sighted, the result was that she took him in her arms,
kissed him and wept for joy. Then she ran happily to
tell the good news to her other sons.

"Where is he? Where is he?" they all shouted.

"Bring him here and let us see!"

"Sit down and I'll bring him – but mind you don't hurt him now," she warned.

"What? Hurt our brother?" they protested. "Bring him quickly!" But when they saw Swot, they cried out:

"Bah! He can't be our brother, he's as small as a man. He *is* a man. Let's eat him!" They were about to fall on him when their mother shouted:

"Are you mad? You wouldn't eat my baby, would you – your own brother?"

"But he's such a wee thing," they insisted, "even for a man. He can't possibly be a dragon."

"He's had a hard life, children," the mother dragon explained. "He fell into the hands of cruel humans, and they forced him to work hard and long, with very little food. That's why he's stayed so small. But he's just as savage as you are, can't you see?"

That was all the thirty-nine dragon brothers

needed to convince them. They all hugged Swot in turn, then one by one they lifted him onto their shoulders, delighted to have found a new brother to play with, even if he was so small. But then, hadn't Swot's father once spoken of him as the little runt?

Swot stayed for three days with the dragons, and as you can imagine he had great fun with his new companions. When the fourth day came he asked their mother if he could go and visit his cousins, the dragons who lived in the tower down the road.

"But I want two of my brothers to come with me," he added. "When they see I'm no bigger than a man, they'll want to gobble me up unless there's someone with me to explain."

Two of the dragons volunteered at once and soon they were on their way to the other towers. Swot stayed three days in each with his other "cousins" and had a whale of a time. The dragons were glad to see him too, and eager to hear how he had fallen among humans and managed to make his escape.

At the third tower, he decided to ask some questions of his own when they had finished with theirs. Very casually, he enquired whether the countryside that lay beyond was beautiful, and if any of them ever went that way. But of course his real reason for asking was to learn about the terrible monster.

"We never go a step in that direction!" the dragons replied in horror, "and if you know what's good for you, nor will you. Between the mountains and the sea there lurks the huge and fearsome creature who gave birth to our mothers. It is such a terrifying size that when it's lying on the ground, its head brushes the clouds. When it is hungry, it bites off great chunks from the mountains, and when it is thirsty, it drinks so much water that the sea-bed is laid bare. We'd be mad to go that way when it doesn't even care we are its grandchildren. If it ever found us, it would chew all forty of us up – and the other eighty, for that matter."

"But couldn't you think of a way to sneak up on this monster and kill it somehow?" Swot enquired.

"How could we get up close without it seeing us? We're not exactly small ourselves," the dragons replied. "And as for killing it, do you imagine that would be an easy matter?"

"If you're a little chap like me, perhaps it would," said Swot to their surprise. "Here's what I'm going to do. I'll creep up slowly on the monster, wriggle inch by inch beneath its belly, and then you'll see what happens! All I need is a nice long skewer and a bow. Arm yourselves with your bows, too. Follow me till you're in shooting distance, and then I promise you we'll put paid to this monster."

"You bet we will!" the dragons cried. "And we'll bring our cousins along as well, so we can all shoot it together."

"That's just what I was going to suggest," said

83

Swot. "Why don't a couple of you run off and fetch them? And don't forget – they must all bring bows and arrows, lots of arrows!"

Soon they were all assembled, a scaly dragon-army of one hundred and twenty fearsome warriors. And at their head marched little Swot, the smallest "dragon" of them all. After a whole week on the road they finally saw the monster in the distance. They got a little closer and then the sky went dark and hid the sun. At this point all the dragons lost their nerve. All except one, of course, and that was Swot.

"We're not going any further," the others told him.

"All right, but be ready though. And bows drawn, remember."

Bent low, he crept from bush to bush, came right up to the monster and fearlessly wormed his way beneath its massive body. Then he drove the long skewer straight into its belly. The monster bent its towering head to see what enemy had struck at it so painfully, and in doing so received an arrow in the eye. It gave a roar of agony, and, seeing the monster wounded, the other dragons came out from their hiding-place and showered it with arrows. With hideous screams, the monster writhed and thrashed, uprooting great rocks in its death-throes till the whole mountain shook and rumbled and the sea was whipped to foam. Finally it collapsed in a lifeless heap, its quivering body bristling with arrows. It was a sight you would not wish on your worst enemy.

When all was over and the monster had given its last shudder, Swot called out to his 'brothers':

"Now we must throw it in the sea. We can't have a dead body blocking up the road."

"That's our job," one of the dragons answered. "You just take a rest. Why don't you cool off with a little walk?"

There was nothing Swot wanted more. He made a detour round the busy dragons and continued on his way.

He walked for twenty days until he came to the country of the castle with three maidens, where the magic soil was to be found. He had not yet reached the city when he met his first surprise. In a field beside the road he saw men gathering in the harvest. At least, that's what they looked as if they were doing, but the strange thing was that none of them were moving. Swot went up and spoke to one, but got no response at all. He gave him a nudge, but still there was no sign that the man had heard. Then Swot remembered what the book had told him about the sudden, months-long sleep that fell on people in these parts. Being a kind-hearted lad, he was upset to see them standing there like statues, but then he told himself, 'Maybe it's better that they're all asleep. Now there will be no one to stop me taking

the magic earth. But who's going to let me into the palace to see the princess? Never mind. Let's see how things turn out as I go along.'

He walked into the city and looked around him, filled with curiosity. Not a soul was moving. The shops were all open, and filled with people sleeping on their feet. A housewife was carrying a basket, a porter was frozen in mid-step with a sack upon his shoulders, a woman held the money in her hand to buy tomatoes and a fat boy had fallen asleep with half a doughnut sticking from his mouth. It was clear the sickness had fallen on them in the middle of a busy working-day.

Swot was so fascinated by all he saw in the sleeping city's streets that before he knew it he found himself outside the palace. Three guards stood on either side of the great gate, their eyes shut fast but still holding their tall spears and shields. The door which led into the courtyard stood wide open, so he went inside. In its centre stood a lemon-tree, with railings all around to protect this tree and the precious earth that it was planted in, a rich, dark-red soil which looked just as it had been described in all the books he'd read. So this was what he had overcome so many obstacles to find! He scooped up a handful and put it in his bag, thanking his lucky stars for leading him to his goal.

To his first goal, that is, for young Swot had other business still in hand. He turned towards the palace and crept in with beating heart, rather overawed by the great and impressive building, although he was a prince himself. In the first high chamber sat the king, fast asleep upon his throne, dressed in his royal robes and golden crown. In one hand he held a string of amber beads. Swot hesitated for a moment and then took them. "These beads may come in handy," he decided. On another throne beside the king the queen slept like a stone, still holding up her fan. Swot took this too, for the same reason, and went on with his exploring. Going into another room, he found a lovely maiden dressed in splendid clothes. It was clear she was a princess, but something told him she was not the one he sought. Even so, he needed something that belonged to her, so he took the golden comb that held her hair. In the next room he found another princess sleeping upright, and she was even lovelier than the first. From her breast he took a brooch that was set with precious stones. Sure now that he would find the third and fairest of the princesses, he hurried to the room beyond. And when indeed he found her there, his heart began to beat as if his chest would burst. She was the very image of the princess who had visited him in his dreams. He gazed upon her loveliness for hours, hardly able to drag his unwilling feet away. He longed to stay until the girl awoke, but he knew it was his duty to take the magic earth back to his father. Besides, who knew how many weeks might pass before all these sleeping people came to life again? It seemed the princess had been sewing something when she fell asleep, for on her knees there lay a half-worked piece of embroidery. Swot took the needlework, then carefully folded it and put it in his pocket. Next, after a moment's thought, he slipped off the ring he wore, which had his name, Demos, engraved upon it, exchanging it for hers, which also bore her name: Violetta. Finally he bent and kissed her tenderly, first on one cheek then the other, and such was the love that went into those kisses that two full-blown roses fell to earth. 'Now we are engaged,' he told himself. 'When she wakes up she will realise what has happened, and if she moves heaven and earth to find me, as I know she will, she will become my wife.' As he was leaving, he stooped to take the roses, and then he remembered how the book had told him that these people could only be cured of their sleeping sickness if love made six roses fall to earth. 'Now two have fallen,' Swot told himself, 'and I shall take them with me, for who knows, they may have the power to help me when the going gets hard.'

With these words he turned and hurried from the palace. After walking fast for several days, he found himself once more at the spot where the monster had been slain. All this time his 'brothers' and his 'cousins' the dragons had been struggling to roll the dead beast down into the sea. It was a daunting task, but they were almost done, and now the road was open.

Just as the monster crashed into the waves, they looked up and saw Swot.

"Where have you been all this time?" they asked. "We thought we'd lost you."

"Oh, I was up on the mountain over there, admiring your strength," Swot answered innocently.

The dragons believed him.

"Let's go and celebrate our victory, then," they said. And they all got together at the first tower, where they had a wonderful time but drank so much wine that by the morning they were drunk as lords. Swot took care not to follow their example and secretly poured away the wine they gave him. Eventually, when the earth was shaking with their drunken snores, he sized the opportunity to escape.

For three days he walked on undisturbed, but on the fourth he heard a thundering of feet and angry voices far behind. It was the dragons coming after him. When they discovered he had slipped away in secret, without even saying goodbye to the mother-dragon, they realised his tale about being her long-lost son was all a lie and that, as they had suspected from the start, he was a man. Furious at being tricked, they came in hot pursuit, determined to make a meal of him in spite of all the help he'd given them in slaying the monster. The brave lad sprinted to escape them but they ran even faster. To make matters worse, the road was now becoming very muddy, and although Swot tried to find a way around he soon found himself unable to move a step in any direction. The dragons were almost upon him when he suddenly thought of the magic roses. He threw one down and immediately the mud stopped sucking at his feet. Now he could run across the boggy ground as easily as on solid rock. But it was another matter for the dragons. They floundered around and soon found themselves sunk almost to their necks. For all their efforts, they had to give up the chase and go back home, plastered in mud from head to toe and in a very bad temper.

Swot walked on for a few more days until he reached the spot where he had parted from his brothers. He lifted up the stone where they had placed their rings, but only found his own. This meant his brothers must have given up and turned back, and he knew they would be furious at their failure. If he went and told the cowards he had brought the magic earth, who knows what they might do to him. 'But I'll tell them all the same,' he finally decided, 'and if it's earth they want, it's earth they'll get.' And with this thought he bent and took a handful of the soil at his feet. He would give them that if they demanded it, but keep the magic earth hidden safely in his bag.

Swot walked over to the nearby town and went into an inn to spend the night. Now this was the same place where his brothers had stayed, and from the innkeeper he learned that those two fine young princes, who had arrived with fifty mounted soldiers each, were soon obliged to sell off all the horses and send their men away because they no longer had the money left to feed them. They had thrown such wild parties at the inn, drunk and danced so many nights away, that in the end they were left without a penny to their name. They were forced to take whatever jobs they could find to stay alive, and now they were working for a crust of bread, one at a cookhouse and the other at a baker's. Swot went out and found them. They were such a pitiful sight it was enough to make you weep.

"Come on, let's go home," he said.

"But how can we go back empty-handed?" they protested. "Or have you found the magic earth?"

"I have," Swot replied, "and now father will be able to see again."

"Then you must let us have our share," his eldest brother insisted. "We must all have some earth to give him."

"Certainly," replied young Swot. "Here you are." And he gave them some of the soil he had scooped up from the roadside, which was good for nothing.

They set off on the long trek home, but as they

walked the two bigger brothers kept whispering to each other.

"We must get rid of him," said the eldest.

"Once and for all," replied the other, "but how?"

The answer came to them when they found a well by the road. It had no bucket, but only a length of rope.

"One of us will have to tie himself to the rope and go down for some water," said the eldest brother.

"It would be better if the lightest of us three went down," added the second brother.

And so it was decided that Swot should be the one.

They tied the rope around his waist, began to lower him down the well, but suddenly pretended they had lost their grip and let him fall. Without a word to one another they turned and continued on their journey homewards.

It took them three more months of travelling to

get back to their father's palace. The moment they arrived they ran to find him.

"Have you brought the earth?" the king demanded anxiously.

"Of course we have!" his sons replied, feeling very pleased with themselves. "Here, let's put it on your eyes."

As they were mixing it into a paste, the queen came in. Delighted to see the princes safely home, she hugged them both and showered them with kisses.

"Well done, boys," she said, "but where's your little brother?"

"We don't know," replied the princes shamelessly. "He was so beside himself with jealousy when he learned that we had found the magic earth that he just ran off, and we haven't seen him since."

"Are we going to waste our time discussing Swot?" the king demanded. "Put the earth on my eyes, and quickly!"

So they did as they were told. And all that came of it, of course, was that his poor blind eyes felt sorer still.

"I'll never believe in doctors again as long as I live!" the king cried angrily. "No more medicine for me, however bad I get!"

We left Swot sitting at the bottom of the well. A whole day passed, then two, then three. Luckily, there was not much water down there, just a little pool in the deepest spot, and so he made himself as comfortable as he could, all the while hoping that God would take pity on him – and on his father as well, for those blind eyes would never see again if Swot were to die down this dark, damp hole. As for the lovely princess, all his hopes of seeing her once more were now a fading dream. "I only pray she doesn't put her life in danger by coming to look for me," he thought. And at the memory of the two kisses he had planted on her cheeks, a warm glow spread through him, a glow that quickly changed to cold despair when he looked up at the tiny circle of blue sky above.

But suddenly he remembered: One of the roses had saved him when he was trying to escape the dragons. "Could the other save me now?" he wondered, and tossed it in the puddle at his feet. Yes, it could! By some miracle, water began to gush up from the bottom of the well. Soon it had reached Swot's knees, and then his waist, and in no time at all it was lapping at his chin. By now his feet could no longer touch the bottom, but he was a good swimmer and in no danger of drowning. Up and up the water rose, and up swam young Swot with it, until at last he reached the top and jumped out, soaked but safe.

His first thought as he scrambled to his feet was for the magic earth. What if the water had got into his bag and washed it all away? But his fears were groundless. Not a single drop had found its way into

the bag, and the earth, the princess's needlework, the fan and all the other things he had taken from the palace were quite unharmed. After all, if a miracle is worked for your own good, how can it possibly work against you? And so our hero happily resumed his journey home.

Like his brothers, Swot was three months on the road before he saw his parents' castle in the distance. On arriving, he made his way in secretly and ran to find his mother. The poor woman had given him up for lost, and wept tears of joy to see him.

"What happened to you, son?" she asked, holding him tightly to her breast. "Your brothers said you had disappeared."

"This isn't the time to tell you my adventures, mother," Swot replied, fearing she might not be able to keep her good news to herself. "Just run and put this earth on father's eyes, to make them well again."

"Alas, my child," she answered sadly, "your brothers brought back some of this earth, too. But it didn't work, and now your father doesn't want to hear another word about medicines and doctors' remedies."

"Maybe their earth didn't work, but mine will," Swot insisted. "Go on, mother, I know you'll find some way of persuading him."

At first the king refused to listen to a word about the brave lad and the magic earth, but in the end the queen managed to persuade him, and the moment she mixed some into mud and put it on his eyes the miracle occurred: he could see again! Overcome with joy, he took his youngest son into his arms and kissed him for the first time in his life.

When they saw this, Swot's brothers were beside themselves with jealousy. They went and told their father he had stolen the real earth from them. Alas, the king was all too willing to believe their tale, and in a fit of rage he ordered Swot to be thrown into the dungeons. And that was all the reward the brave young man received for his kind-heartedness.

Six months had passed, with Swot still lying in jail and his mother weeping fit to break her heart, when one evening strangers arrived at the palace from a distant kingdom. And that kingdom was none other than the one where he had gone to find the magic earth.

Now when the people of that kingdom had woken from their sleep and begun to go about their business once again, the king looked for his amber beads and could not find them, the queen searched for her fan but could not see it anywhere, the eldest princess went to put her hair up with her golden comb and discovered it was missing, her younger sister went up to the mirror and saw that her brooch with all its precious stones was no longer on her breast, while the youngest princess of them all reached down for her needlework and realised that it

had disappeared. As she looked down, her eyes fell on her fingers and she saw an unknown ring in place of the one she had been wearing with her name engraved upon it. She drew the ring off and saw that it, too, had letters carved inside it – letters that formed a man's name: Demos. Then she looked to her left and saw a rose-petal lying on the cushion of her chair. She looked to the right and saw another. Immediately she realised that this unknown visitor must have kissed her on both cheeks, and at the thought her face flushed scarlet. She pressed the stranger's ring to her lips and her eyes filled with tears. She was seized with an irresistible longing to see this brave young man who had exchanged his ring for hers. Suddenly a thought came to her. She ran out to the courtyard where the lemon-tree stood, and when she saw the soil around it had been disturbed, she realised that whoever had exchanged her ring for his had come in search of magic earth to heal some blind king. He must be a prince, too, for no common person would have the means to carry out such a long and dangerous mission. So she ran to her father, her mother and her sisters and told them they must go in search of the brave young fellow who had done this daring deed. The two princesses were enthusiastic, but the king and queen were none too keen on the idea. However, the three girls were so insistent that the royal couple at last agreed to let them have their way, though they decided not go themselves. Two trusted officers were appointed to accompany them, along with a dozen soldiers for everyone's protection. The expedition set off in three carriages, but before they left, the three princesses dressed up in men's clothes, cut short their hair and learned to speak and walk in a manly fashion. When their disguise was complete, nobody would ever have guessed that these three noble youths were actually young women.

The officers led the party out of the kingdom by a secret road, and so they did not have to face the dragons, the mud, the whirlwinds or the burning plain.

The three girls already had their plan. Wherever they went, they asked if anyone had heard of a king who had gone blind and then regained his sight. They asked in kingdom after kingdom, but all to no avail, until one day they reached the very kingdom they were seeking. There they were told that the king had indeed been struck by blindness, but had been cured some six months earlier with magic earth brought by his three sons from a faraway land. However, there was some disagreement as to which of the three sons had actually come home with the magic earth. Some said it was the two eldest ones, while others insisted that it was their little brother. "And what is his name?" asked the youngest of the three princesses. "Demos" came the reply.

"Off to the palace!" cried the lovely girl.

"As fast as our feet can carry us!" replied her sisters, laughing happily.

The moment they arrived, they asked to see the king.

"The king received the three young men with open arms, for he could see by their fine clothes and polished manners that they must be princes.

The youngest sister immediately began their story:

"Our father is the ruler of a distant country," she explained, "but he has lost his sight. Not long ago, we heard that you were once blind, too, but were cured when magic earth was rubbed upon your eyes. We have come on this long, long journey to beg you to tell us where we can find this earth which works such miracles."

The king was moved. "I cannot tell you how it pleases me to meet young men who care so much about their father. My two sons had the same tender feelings towards me, and it was they who brought the magic earth which made me well again." And with these words he sent for the two princes.

As soon as they arrived, the youngest princess took one look at their hands and saw that neither of them was wearing her ring, and when she asked them where they had found the earth, they could only give her vague, confused replies.

"Your majesty," the king's young visitor announced, "I am sure your two fine sons are all you say they are, but they seem unable to tell us where they got the earth. Now we have heard you have another son, Demos by name," – the king's face darkened when he heard these words– "and we have also learned that he was with his brothers when they went to find this magic cure. Could we speak with him as well?"

"Alas, young princes," said the king, "why must you grieve my heart by reminding me of a son who

is no longer any son of mine? There is nothing whatsoever he can tell you, and it is not worth your trouble speaking to him."

"But if by any chance he does know something,
we may be able to save our father's sight," the young
princess insisted. "We beg you, noble majesty, to do
us this one favour. It is all we ask."

On hearing for a second time how desperate the
princes were to lift the blindness from their father's
eyes, the king was doubly moved. He decided to
bring Swot to them after all.

"Very well," he said, "let him tell you what he
knows – although I am sure he won't know anything."

But Swot was still chained up in the dungeons.
How could the king possibly let the visitors see him
filthy and in rags?

"I would bring him to you now," the king continued, playing for time, "but unfortunately he is not

here at present. Let us say tomorrow, shall we? And in the meantime, sit down with us to eat and rest your weary legs. Then, when you have had a good night's sleep, we shall meet in the morning and you shall speak with this young man you seem so keen to meet."

Following this, the king called for his chamberlain and spoke to him in private. He ordered Swot to be taken from his cell at once, washed, shaved and given a haircut. Clean clothes were to be laid out for him, freshly pressed, so that when he appeared before the princely visitors next morning, he would look presentable, if not well-fed.

And so the following day they all assembled once again. First came the king and queen, then the three princes from the faraway kingdom, next the king's two eldest sons and finally young Swot himself.

He had guessed what might be in the wind when they took him from his cell, and when he saw the three young princes, he knew at once he had been right.

As for the youngest, she could hardly keep herself from crying out in joy when she saw her ring on the pale young man's finger. Somehow, she managed to disguise her feelings, putting on a show of indifference which deceived everyone but Swot, who had seen his ring upon her hand the moment he came in.

"Now, you," said the king, looking at him coldly, "tell us where your brothers found the magic earth you stole from them. Not that you know, of course!"

"Father," replied young Swot, "the time has come for you to learn what really happened." And then he told him all the dangers he had passed to reach that distant kingdom, how he had found the magic earth, and how his brothers had left him down the well to die.

"Lies! All lies!" his brothers shouted, but instead

of answering them, Swot coolly turned to the three young noblemen who were really princesses in disguise, and taking a string of amber beads from the bag which he was carrying, he said:

"I am sure you recognize these beads. I took them from your father to prove I reached the kingdom where the magic earth is found. Now I return them to you."

"This is all a mystery to me," the king said grumpily.

"Not such a mystery as you think," the queen replied.

"It's perfectly simple," the eldest son replied. "He stole the magic earth from us, and that's the end of it!"

"No need to shout," replied Swot calmly. "If it's an end you want, I'll soon be finished." And with this he began to take out, one by one, the other objects that were in his bag.

"This fan is your mother's, and this golden comb belongs to you," he said, handing them to the eldest of the princes. "This jewelled brooch is yours," he told the second. And turning to the youngest: "As for this embroidery, I believe it is your work. And one more thing – you're not princes at all, but girls dressed up as men!"

"I was taken in completely!" gasped the king.

"I can't say I was," said his wife, with a knowing smile on her lips.

But Swot had more surprises for them. Turning to the youngest princess, he went on: "The ring you are wearing on your finger bears my name, Demos, and this ring on my hand has yours engraved on it. Violetta, they call you. Let's take them off for everyone to see". And removing the two rings, they showed the company the names inside them.

"All this is beyond me!" said the king, scratching his head.

"It's perfectly obvious," the queen replied. "These girls have not come here to find the magic earth, but to find who took it from them. And the princess who is wearing our son's ring has made this long and dangerous journey to follow where her heart was leading: to our dear, brave Demos ."

"Is all this true, girls?" asked the king.

"Every word of it, your majesty!" they cried, pushing Violetta into Demos's waiting arms.

"Then off with their heads!" the king roared to his guards, pointing an angry finger at his eldest sons, who stood there trembling, with faces pale as wax.

"No, father," said the youngest, "they have learned their lesson. What do you say, mother?"

"I say that when there is a wedding to be celebrated, it is a time for evil-doers to be forgiven."

"What are we waiting for, then?" cried the king. "As of tomorrow, the preparations for the wedding shall commence. Send out invitations to all the kings and princes in the neighbouring lands. I intend to hold a celebration which will be remembered for all times!"

As the king had promised, the wedding-feast was unforgettable. Why, even the preparations lasted forty days, and while they were going on the princes from two nearby kingdoms, who had come to lend a hand, fell head over heels in love with Violetta's elder sisters. And so it was not just one marriage ceremony that took place when the great day came, but three.

One more wonder and our tale of Swot is done — not that anyone dreamed of calling him by that rude name, now he was restored to favour. During the wedding, he remembered something he had read in his beloved books: that the long sleep which sometimes fell upon the people of the three brides' country could be lifted if love made six roses fall to earth. At that very moment, the king was telling the grooms to kiss their brides.

"And make sure you do it on both cheeks!" cried Sw.... Forgive me, I meant Demos. So the three princes kissed their royal brides twice each, and as they did so, six roses fluttered from the sky. The spell was broken in their distant kingdom and the people's endless sleeps were over. Not only that, but what had once been a long and dangerous journey was suddenly made easy, for the great obstacles along the way were overcome by the newly-weds' even greater love. Now it became such a short and pleasant trip that everybody made it and lived happily ever after.

My tale is over, and a very good night to you all.

The Magic Mirror

nce upon a time there lived a king and queen who had three children. They were good children, too, but all boys, and good as they were, the royal couple longed to have a baby girl. Night and day the queen asked God to grant them this one favour. Hearing her anxious prayers, He answered, not only granting them the daughter they desired but blessing the child with a beauty such as the world had never seen. The baby was truly a gift of God, and when they placed her in her cradle, she lit the whole room with her radiance. They named her Chryssa, and everyone in the palace came to admire her loveliness. As for her brothers, they never tired of playing with their new sister, dandling her on their knees, holding her in their arms or rocking her to sleep with gentle lullabies. Now the king and queen had the perfect family they wanted.

But soon the queen fell ill, and she had only been a few days on her sick bed when Charon, cruel king of the underworld, came stalking in and carried her off without so much as asking leave. Now there were sobs of grief where happy smiles had reigned before. The poor king moaned and tore his hair, the three boys wept and nobody could comfort them, while little Chryssa, who had lost the comfort of her mother's arms and the warm milk she found there, just opened wide her eyes in puzzlement.

She could not be left unfed for long, so a wet nurse was quickly found to suckle her. She was a young woman, hardly more than a girl, and very, very beautiful. She carried out her tasks with loving care

and showed Chryssa every tenderness. Her brothers, too, shared in this warmth and kindness they now had such great need of. But above all, the girl made every effort to ensure the king was pleased – which indeed he was, for he saw how she had won his children's love by her affection and readiness to help.

Yet was she doing it out of the goodness of her heart, or did her kind attentions have another motive? Unfortunately for the king and his orphaned children, it was the second of these. Behind that smiling face she hid a plan to marry the king one day and be crowned queen. Although she saw that in his grief the king had no eyes for another woman, she did not give up hope but waited patiently.

Meanwhile the children were growing, and with every day that passed young Chryssa became lovelier and more graceful. She adored the nurse who seemed to take such loving care of her, and so did the boys, who now looked on her almost as a mother. The girl knew that the children would help her to achieve her secret goal, but she also knew that her own beauty would be a still more effective weapon, and so she took great pains over her appearance. She even had a magic mirror, and from time to time, as she gazed at her fair reflection in its depths, she would ask:

"Tell me, precious mirror, is there any woman in the world who is lovelier than me?"

And the mirror would answer:

"You are the fairest of them all. No woman on this earth is lovelier than you."

The mirror's reassurance always flattered her immensely, and she would tell herself: 'One day the king's eyes will be opened and he will see me as a woman.' But as this seemed to be a long time happening, she decided to take other steps. She approached the head cook of the palace and won her friendship. Now the king loved this old woman like a mother, and often turned to her for comfort in his grief. She was a simple, honest creature and never suspected ill in others, so she was easily won over by the young nurse who seemed to care so deeply for the royal orphans.

One day, as they were chatting away like two good friends, the conversation turned to the king and his unhappiness. The nurse seized her opportunity and said:

"His majesty really is so miserable! I think the only cure for him is to find the daughter of some nobleman and marry again. The children need a mother, too. If only some kind and caring lady could be found!" She said no more, but these few words were enough. The very next day, the old cook went to see the king.

"Long life to you, my lord," she greeted him. "It tears my heart to see you suffering like this. You cannot spend the rest of your life grieving for a woman who is dead, however adorable she may have been. At this very moment, you have a treasure in your palace, although you do not see it. I know you always listen to me when I speak from the heart, and it's for your own good that I say it: Marry the woman your children have come to love so dearly, and who loves them just as deeply in return."

Now while the king did not say he would follow her advice, he did not reject it either. The old cook ran to the young nurse to tell her what she had achieved. "The rest is up to you," she added when her tale was done.

The nurse jumped for joy. She knew what her next step must be and went immediately to find the children.

"My dears," she said, 'your father has been advised to marry me. If you would like that, too, and I am sure you long for it, then show him how happy it would make you – but only if he asks for your opinion, mind you."

But just as she had known they would, the children ran to the king without waiting to be asked. They fell into his arms, begging him to marry their dear nurse, and a few days later the wedding was celebrated in the little chapel of the palace. At last the nurse's plans had borne their fruit. She was now the children's stepmother, but above all she had achieved her dearest wish and been crowned queen.

At first, life for the children went on as happily as before. They were growing into splendid young people, especially Chryssa, who grew lovelier by the day and whose grace and beauty seemed to flood the palace with a magic light. But at last the hour arrived when her stepmother, seeing her more radiant than ever before, was seized with pangs of jealousy. She ran immediately to ask her magic mirror:

"Is there any woman in the world who is lovelier than me?"

And this time the mirror answered:

"Lovely though you may be, you are not as fair as Chryssa."

The queen could not believe her ears. A jealous rage swelled up inside her, and from that day on she ceased to treat young Chryssa like a daughter and began to look on her as a hated rival. Behind the king's back, she used every cruel means she could invent to make the poor princess look ugly. But all to no avail, for when she went back to her magic mirror and said: "Tell me, precious mirror, is there any woman in the world lovelier than me?" the dreaded answer came again: "Lovely though you may be, you are not as fair as Chryssa." And this time her jealousy was so violent she could hardly keep herself from shattering the mirror.

Soon after this, disaster struck the palace. The king fell ill and died. Now the children had lost both their parents and were at the mercy of their wicked stepmother, who was free at last to treat them as cruelly as she wished. She dressed Chryssa in rags and set her to scrubbing floors and scouring greasy saucepans. She would not even let her wash, and soon her beauty was hidden beneath her tattered clothes and layers of grime. Now the mirror gave once more the answer that the wicked queen so longed to hear: "No woman in the world is lovelier than you!"

Chryssa suffered but said nothing, and although her brothers wept to see her in this sorry state, there was nothing they could do. As for the old cook, she bitterly regretted having helped the wicked nurse to marry her master and become queen.

In the end, their life became so miserable that Chryssa's brothers could no longer bear it. They decided to take their sister and run away. They made their farewells to the cook in secret, and she gave them all they would need for their escape.

They walked and walked, without once stopping to look back. By the time night fell, they were in a wild and empty place. And then, to make things worse, a violent storm broke on them. There was a rumbling of thunder, the skies were torn by lightning flashes and then the heavens opened and the rain poured down in torrents. The storm eventually moved on, but by now the children were soaked to the skin and trembling with cold. Then, in the darkness, they saw a dim light flickering. They stumbled on towards it and soon made out the dark shape of a castle, all in shadow except for the faint light coming from one window. They beat their fists upon the door, and after what seemed an age an old lady came to open it. She was a kind-hearted soul, and when she saw how wet and miserable the young people were, her heart went out to them. Bringing the children in, she gave them dry clothes to change into and sat them down beside the fire. Once its flames had warmed them she served them bowls of steaming soup, then sent them off to bed. Only when they woke up in the morning, feeling somewhat stronger, did she ask them whose children they were and how they had come to be out in the wilds on such a stormy night. The youngsters could not find words to thank the lady for her kindness. They told her they were orphans – but without revealing that their father was a king– and that they had fallen into the clutches of an evil stepmother who wanted to destroy them. And so they had run away from home, not even knowing which way they were headed.

"You can stay, children," the kind old lady reassured them. "Once I had a husband here who took good care of me, and fine hardworking sons and lovely daughters. How I come to be alone and helpless is a long, sad story, and now is not the time to tell it. Stay here and be a comfort to me, children, out of the way of the wicked woman who is searching for you, for I find it hard to manage on my own."

The young people decided to accept the kind

old lady's offer. Besides, they were so weak and tired after their terrible night in the storm that they needed time to recover.

Let us leave them resting in the castle and go to see what their wicked stepmother had been doing in the meantime. As soon as she realised that Chryssa and her brothers must have run away, she tore her hair with rage. Soldiers were immediately sent in search of them. Though they hunted high and low, they found no trace of the children and decided they must have perished in the terrible storm. The queen pretended to be heart-broken, but as soon as she was alone she ran to question her mirror:

"Tell me, precious mirror: Is there any woman in the world more beautiful than me ?" And the mirror answered:

"You are the loveliest of them all."

Now she was sure that Chryssa must be dead, and she danced for joy.

Meanwhile, at the castle, the children were recovering. Once Chryssa had got her strength back, after the long months of slaving for her stepmother and the exhausting night spent in the storm, she not only regained her former beauty but grew lovelier by the day. The boys would go off hunting and bring back hares, quails or partridges. They also tended the old lady's garden and looked after the few farm animals she kept, so there was food to spare and they all lived well. But their sister never left the castle. She was afraid that word of her presence might get out and that their evil stepmother would find them, for they had realised by now that she must be a witch. So Chryssa spent her days inside, sometimes doing needlework and sometimes helping the old lady in the kitchen while she listened to her tales of life at the castle in the good old days.

The kind old lady opened all the rooms and showed them to her. There were forty in all. "In this room here, with the gilded bed, kings and queens have slept," she told the girl, "and this one here was the prince's room, in the happy times when royalty often came to stay. But when the I was left here all alone, then everyone forgot me, except for one kind young man who loves me like a mother. He's a prince, too, and an only child, so he'll be king one day. But it hasn't made him proud and he drops in from time to time to make sure I have everything I need. It's been a while since he last called by, but I know he'll be here soon."

She had hardly finished speaking when from the courtyard down below they heard the clip-clop of horses' hooves and the clattering of ironbound wheels. They looked out and saw a splendid carriage drawn by four fine horses pull up outside the castle.

"That's him!" cried the old lady, as a richly dressed young man stepped down from the carriage. "Stay here and meet him. It won't do you any harm to say good morning to him."

"But I'm afraid!" cried Chryssa. "My brothers warned me that no stranger must ever learn a girl is staying here. He may mention it to others, not knowing it might harm me, and then word could get back to my stepmother."

"Very well, my dear, just as you wish," the kind old lady answered, "but at least slip into the kitchen, so you can see him through the serving-hatch. If you don't want to meet him face to face, at least do me this favour."

She said that because she remembered how, long ago, when she had been a girl herself, she too had hidden out of sight and peeped through a chink to see the prince who would one day be her husband. She had never forgiven herself, not for having looked, but for having done so without her parents' knowledge. So now she not only gave Chryssa her permission to gaze upon the prince, but almost begged her to. For once she had set eyes on him, who knew what might follow?

So, peering through the serving-hatch, Chryssa secretly watched the handsome prince. She admired his tall, strong figure and noted how kindly and politely he treated the old lady.

"Did you see him, my dear?" she asked eagerly as the carriage rolled away.

"Yes, I saw him," answered Chryssa, blushing to the roots of her hair. The kind old lady noted this and secretly rejoiced.

But now it is time for us to leave the old lady's castle, or the castle of the forty chambers as it was sometimes called, and return once more to the palace of the wicked stepmother.

It had been a long time now since the children disappeared, and the wicked queen had no more anxieties on Chryssa's score. She was sure the girl was dead.

138

The Magic Mirror

139

One Sunday, she was getting ready to go to church, to thank the Virgin Mary that everything had turned out as she wished. As she stood before the mirror, adding the finishing touches to her dress and admiring the result, she felt the need to hear once more that she was the loveliest woman in the world.

"Tell me, precious mirror, is there any woman in the world who is fairer than I am?" she asked, sure of the answer she would hear. But the reply that came was this:

"Lovely though you may be, you are not as fair as Chryssa."

The news was like a slap across the face. No question of church now! She must find Chryssa, and find her quickly! Turning once more to the mirror, she learned the girl was hiding in the castle of the forty chambers.

Without wasting a moment, she ran to an attic where there was an old trunk full of party clothes.

Rummaging through it, she pulled out handfuls of false jewellery, then went back to her room, opened the silver casket that stood upon her dressing-table and drew out a gold ring with a diamond shining like the sun. Kissing it, she murmured: "You will do my work for me!" After that she muttered magic words over the ring, kissed it once again and put it in a bag along with the false jewels. Finally, she dressed herself in a man's clothes, like a peddler, found a tray which she would hang in front of her when the right time came, and left the palace secretly, clutching the bag of jewels.

Just before she reached the old lady's castle, she laid the jewels out on the tray, the gold ring with its shining diamond in the middle, then went and stood beneath the castle windows, calling out her wares.

The boys were out hunting at the time, and Chryssa was hidden away in her room, working on a piece of embroidery, so it was the old lady who heard the peddler's cries.

'What's a peddler doing in this wild place?' she wondered. 'It's never happened before; I'd better go and see.'

She went down and saw the jewels, and her eye fell immediately upon the diamond ring, of course.

'I think I'll buy this for young Chryssa,' she told herself, lifting the ring from the tray to admire its gleaming workmanship.

The 'peddler's' eyes gleamed, too, with wicked satisfaction.

'Now we shall see who is more beautiful!' she muttered to herself.

"How much do you want for it?" the old lady asked.

"I like your face," replied the peddler, "so I'll agree to any price you name."

"No, it's a fine stone and I'll pay you what it's worth," the honest old lady insisted. "I'll just go up and get the money." And with these words she put the ring back on the tray.

But the evil queen was afraid the old lady might change her mind and not come down again.

"No, take it, lady!" she protested. "You don't look the kind of person who would trick me. Take it, and pay me when I pass by again tomorrow." And thrusting the ring into the old lady's hand, the 'peddler' walked off, trying hard not to dance for joy.

"Chryssa, come and see what I've got for you!" the old lady called.

"Ah, it's lovely!" cried Chryssa in delight. "But you really shouldn't go to such expense. Why are you always so kind to me, you dear old thing?"

"Because I had a daughter once," the old lady sighed, "and I lost her when she was just your age, my child."

"What a beautiful ring it is!" Chryssa murmured. I'll put it on the moment my brothers come home.

They'll be so pleased!" And taking the old lady in her arms she kissed her again and again, so pleased was she with her gift.

But once the girl had got back to her room, the temptation to try on the ring was too great to resist. She slipped it on her finger... and then, with a moan that sounded as if her soul were escaping from her body, she sank unconscious to the floor.

Her brothers returned at sunset, tired from the hunt but loaded down with game. They called up to their sister to show her all they'd caught, but received no answer. They called once more, but again got no reply. Then they ran up to Chryssa's room, with the old lady puffing behind them, and could not believe the sight that met their eyes. There lay their sister, dead. They wept and tore their hair, they beat their fists against the wall, while the good old lady shed even more tears than she had for her own children. Day after day they mourned, unable to bring themselves to bury her, in the hope that some miracle might still occur. Yet perhaps that very miracle was taking place before their eyes – for instead of fading with her death, Chryssa's loveliness seemed to grow greater by the day. Yet still she did not wake, and so, when forty days had passed, they built a casket with a crystal cover and laid the girl inside. The brothers were so heartbroken that they could not bear to spend another moment in the castle, but decided to sail as far away as they could find a ship to carry them. Before they left, they locked all the upstairs chambers and gave the bunch of keys to the old lady, including the golden one which opened Chryssa's room.

"Throw those wretched keys into the sea, lads," she said, waving them away. What could I do with them? Go round opening doors and breaking my heart to see the chambers empty, or unlock Chryssa's room and see her lying dead? Throw the whole bunch in the sea, I tell you, and may I never set eyes on them again! Now farewell, and God be with you."

The boys took the keys, hugged the old lady with tears in their eyes and set off for the seashore. As their ship left harbour, they tossed the keys over the side, determined never to return from their voyage into the unknown. They were gone, and the poor old lady was alone once more.

Some time later, a local fisherman landed a huge salmon, such a fine fat specimen, he decided he would try to sell it at the palace. Now who should he meet when he arrived but the prince himself, who immediately bought the fish for a handful of gold florins! The fisherman's luck was in and so was the prince's, though as yet he did not know it. He took the salmon straight to the kitchens, and when the cooks opened up its belly, what should tumble out but a great bunch of keys, all rusty save for one of

gleaming gold. The prince had no idea what keys these were or who they might belong to, but he was curious to learn. So he sent for his father's herald and told him to go from house to house until he found their owner. Eventually the man arrived at a castle in a wild and empty place and questioned the sad old woman who met him at the gate. "There's no need to ask any further," she replied. "The keys are mine. I ordered them to be thrown into the sea because I could not bear the sight of them."

The herald returned to the prince to report what he had learned, and from the man's description it was clear the keys were from the castle with the forty chambers. Now this was the same prince that loved the old lady like a mother, the one Chryssa had gazed on from her hiding place.

Worried that all might not be well with the old lady, the prince hastened to the castle and asked her why she had ordered the keys to be thrown into the sea.

She told him the whole story: how, when she had been all alone in the world, God had sent her three fine boys and a girl who radiated loveliness and grace. But now the castle was empty once again and the beautiful maiden lay in a glass coffin in the room which only the golden key would open.

"Then I shall go and see her," the young prince said at once.

"What is there to see, lad?" sighed the lady. "Lovely though she is, she lies in a sleep from which she will never wake. It would only grieve you to see her. Better not to go."

But the prince went up to her chamber all the same, and at the sight which met his eyes he stood entranced. There in a crystal casket lay a maiden whose loveliness no words could describe. He could have gone on gazing at her face for ever, but the longer his eyes rested on her beauty, the more his heart ached at her cruel fate. Yet still he could not find the strength to leave, but sat there with his eyes fixed on her face. Even when the room grew dark he did not move.

"What, still here?" cried the old lady when she came up to investigate. "The king and queen will be worried sick about you. They'll have men searching for you everywhere by now. Go home, young prince. I'm sure that one day you will find another girl to make you happy."

But the prince would not listen to a word she said. He spent the first night by the sleeping beauty's casket, then the second. It was not until the third day that he was found by the soldiers sent out by the king in search of him. The young man knew he had no choice but to follow them back to his father. He made a vow never to return to the castle with the forty chambers, for he knew that if he saw the princess ever again he would lie down at her side and kill himself.

He made as if to leave the chamber, but had hardly taken two paces when he stopped and told himself:

"I must have some token to remember her by. I will take her ring, and then she will be in my thoughts for ever."

Going to the casket, he lifted the crystal cover and drew off the ring. As he did so, Chryssa sighed, slowly opened her eyes, sat up and said:

"Ah, how heavily I must have slept! But now I feel as fresh as the morning dew."

Then she saw the handsome young prince standing before her and her face lit up with joy, for since the moment she had gazed on him in secret, his features had been engraved upon her memory. Beside himself with happiness, the prince took her hand and helped her from the casket, then folded her in his arms and carried her gently down to the carriage which was waiting. Chryssa was sure she must

151

be living in a dream, so happy was her awakening.
And the kind old lady, who had witnessed the whole
scene, bade the couple farewell with eyes blurred by
her tears. For the first time in her life, she was con-
tent that she would be alone.

The very next day, preparations started for the
wedding. Tailors set to work on a gold-embroidered
bridal gown, lambs and calves were readied for the
table, and the king sent heralds out to every corner
of his kingdom to invite his people to a splendid
double ceremony. For not only was the prince to be
given Chryssa's hand in marriage but the king, who
was an old man now, would appoint his only son to
rule as monarch in his stead. Among those to whom
invitations were sent out were the kings and queens
of all the neighbouring countries. And without suspecting who the bride might be, the queen who had
once been Chryssa's nurse, then her stepmother and
now her deadly rival was among the first to arrive.

She had come not because she felt it was a matter of politeness, but to have the satisfaction of outshining the poor bride and dazzling all the other guests with her radiant beauty. After all, she told herself, now Chryssa was lying lifeless in the castle with the forty chambers, who could be lovelier than she?

But when the ceremony started and she saw the bride, the wicked stepmother almost fell lifeless to the ground herself, choked by her rage. She was so beside herself with fury that for a while she could only gnash her teeth and snarl. But she soon realised that the last thing she must do was draw attention to herself. Above all, she must not let Chryssa see her, so she crept into a corner and racked her evil brains for a solution.

"I must set my magic spells to work once more," she finally decided.

She spent a sleepless night, working magic arts to achieve her wicked goal, and before the sun had risen her devilish plan was ready. It was perfect in its simplicity: with one prick of a tiny pin, Chryssa would disappear for ever.

When morning came, the wicked queen went in search of her victim and found her sitting in the garden. Chryssa leapt up in fear of the unwelcome visitor.

"Don't worry, my dear," she said in honeyed tones. "I come as a friend, a true friend. Ah, how I have missed you!" And she folded the girl in her arms. Chryssa had hardly time to wonder at this unexpected tenderness before the magic pin was plunged into her head, and on the instant the bride of but one day was transformed into a frightened little bird that flew off to hide in a shady corner of the garden. Moments later a heartbreaking warble came from among the leaves, a song so sad it would have torn your heart to hear it.

The cunning queen sped back to her palace, and

when her mirror announced that once again she was the loveliest woman in the world, she could not hold back a laugh of triumph.

As for young Chryssa, now a little bird, she flew from branch to branch and wept. The new king, her husband of one night, went almost wild with grief at the loss of his dear wife. But it was as though the earth had swallowed her, and although they searched the palace, the garden, the city and the whole kingdom, the new queen was nowhere to be found.

The sad song of the little bird filled the garden all day long, yet who could have imagined that it was young queen Chryssa?

Only the gardener's curiosity was roused.

"The poor wee creature! What can trouble it?" he wondered, and following the song he came upon the tiny bird perched on a twig, tears streaming from its eyes.

"Ah, little one, why is your song so sad?" the kind

man asked, not dreaming for a moment he would get an answer.

"My poor head aches so terribly!" replied the bird. And the gardener's mouth dropped open with astonishment.

"What can I do to help you, little bird?" he asked when he had got his voice back.

"Tell the king about my pain," the bird replied.

"And if I do, what then?" he asked again. But the bird seemed not to hear and gave no answer.

"Tell me, why should I risk such a foolish thing?" the gardener insisted. But again his question went unanswered.

"The king would take me for a madman, little friend," the gardener protested. But yet again there came no answer to his question, only a few sad notes of bird song.

The poor man shook his head and walked away.

"I really must be losing my wits, if I thought I

had a conversation with a bird," he murmured, shaking his head in wonderment. "Imagine what would happen to me if I went and told his majesty!"

And so he went to have a sleep instead, hoping that by the time he woke he would no longer fancy he was hearing things. But when day came, the words he had heard the previous evening were still ringing in his ears. And immediately he went out into the garden, the sad song started up once more, and this time sadder still. Then came a new surprise, for now the song had words! And it had to be the bird that sang them, for there was no other person in the garden.

Here is how the song went:

> *'Gardener, oh gardener dear,*
> *The king's lunch will be spoiled*
> *Unless you run and bring him here,*
> *So the witch's magic's foiled.'*

"Now I really have gone out of my mind!" groaned the poor gardener. "I'm hearing voices!"

But the song went on:

'If he does not come to see,
Burned both lunch and tree will be.
So if you love me, gardener dear,
Hurry off and bring him here!'

But instead of going to the king, the gardener ran and hid in his cottage, afraid that if he heard any more voices he would go stark, staring mad.

Lunchtime came, and the new king went hungry. All the dishes the cooks had prepared for him were mysteriously burned. And in the garden, the tree the little bird was perched on withered and died. Next day it was the same: Once again the food was all burnt and another tree had died. But the young king was so unhappy anyway that he hardly noticed. The third day was like the second and the first. This time the king stirred himself and went to scold the cook. He called for the gardener, too, and asked him angrily:

"How can you leave the trees unwatered, when you can see they're dying?"

Now the gardener had no choice but to tell the king about his strange experience with the bird.

"And where is this bird?" the king demanded.

The man took him to the garden, where by now the bird's song sounded more like broken-hearted sobs. A lump came into the king's throat as he listened, and his thoughts flew to the young wife he had lost so suddenly. "That must be how my poor darling cries, wherever she is now," he told himself. But as soon as they came closer and the bird caught sight of the king, it stopped crying and began to flutter round him, letting out a stream of happy cheeps. A moment later and it settled on his shoulder. The king gently caught it in his hand. The bird made no attempt to get away, but settled in his palm as if it had come home to nest.

"Does your head hurt, then, little bird?" the king asked softly, and without waiting for an answer began to stroke its head. At once his fingers found the head of the pin. "What can this be?" he wondered. "Perhaps that's why its head is hurting so." And with these words he gently drew the sharp pin out. I am sure you have already guessed what happened next. Instead of the bird, which vanished in a flash, the king found himself holding the hand of his beloved Chryssa, who had appeared before him in its place and whose beauty dimmed the sun itself.

"My darling!" she cried, and threw herself into his arms weeping with joy, mingling her tears with his upon their cheeks. As for the kind gardener, he left them locked in their embrace and ran to tell everyone the happy news.

A great feast was held at the palace to celebrate queen Chryssa's return.

Happy days now blessed the loving couple, and in the course of time their love bore fruit in the shape of a delightful little daughter.

While the royal couple were enjoying their happiness, the wicked stepmother was far away in her palace, getting ready for a glittering reception to be held in a neighbouring kingdom. She stood before the mirror putting the final touches to her appearance, admiring her beauty and smugly imagining the impression she would make on the foreign king and all his noble guests. She finished painting her lips and eyes, put on her richest and most sparkling jewellery, gazed once more in the mirror and decided she had never looked so lovely in her life. The temptation to hear the mirror's flattering words again was more than the vain queen could resist. It would set the seal on the pride and satisfaction that she felt. But when the answer came, and she heard instead that Chryssa was the loveliest woman in existence, her world collapsed around her. Her eyes went dark as breaking thunderclouds and foam gushed from her lips in frothing torrents. Madness seized her, and in her frenzy she ripped the jewels from her body. Pearl necklaces, finely worked gold bracelets, emerald pins and diamond earrings were flung savagely to the floor.

Plunging cruel fingers into her elaborately dressed hair, she tore out whole tufts by the roots. Unable to control herself, she threw her arms about and stamped furiously round the room until at last she stepped upon the scattered pearls, her feet rolled out from under her, and she fell and hurt her face so badly that one eye puffed up purple, her nose swelled out of shape and – as her mirror would have told her if she had dared to ask – there was now no uglier woman in the world! From this moment, the queen had only one thought in her mind: to be re-venged on Chryssa.

"I'll tear her limb from limb!" she screeched. "She won't escape me this time!" And what should happen as she raged and ranted? Yes, her feet rolled out from under her again!

"Aah! My leg!" she screamed, trying without success to stagger to her feet. Scrabbling for a stick, she eventually managed to drag herself upright and hobble off to bed, so eaten up with wounded pride and hatred that she did not even feel her bruises.

She did not close an eye the whole night long, but it was not her aches and pains that stopped her sleeping. Her mind was working feverishly to find a way to rid herself of Chryssa without anyone suspecting. In the end she hit upon a plan, and this time it was still more devilish than the last.

She was sure she would still find Chryssa in the place where she had worked her magic in the garden.

"I must get myself ready and go there as fast as possible!" she told herself. How fast that would be, when she couldn't walk a step without a crutch, she didn't stop to ask. "She won't escape me this time. With my walking-stick to help me, I'll get there and destroy her!" All this time, without intending to, she had been hobbling towards the mirror.

And what did she see there? Her nose had swelled up like a sausage, one eye was black and blue, her cheeks and chin were torn with bloody scratches – and as for what was left of her once lovely hair, it would be kinder not to say. She was driven to such fury by her hideous appearance that she took it out upon the mirror – or on the face she saw in it, if you prefer – beating her fists upon the glass till they were black with bruises, too. Eventually she came to her senses. "I'd better not break the mirror," she decided in the end. "I'll be needing it again to tell me what I want to hear. Besides, it's time I got myself ready." With these words, she limped off to find some brown dye and painted her face and hands as brown as chestnuts. Then she dyed her hair jet black, dressed up in gipsy clothes, plucked up her courage and took a last look in the mirror. What she saw was even uglier than before: a fat-nosed gipsy woman, swarthy, lumpish-faced and lame.

"But I don't care," she told herself. "Once that other creature's dead – curse her! – I'll get my beauty back, and then everyone will admire and honour me again."

Then she hobbled painfully to a cupboard, took out a bag of magic potions and, leaning heavily on her stick, limped towards Chryssa's palace as fast as her injured leg would carry her.

When she arrived, she told them she was a healer who knew many remedies and had a cure for every illness known to man. Now quite by chance, Chryssa had been worried about her daughter for some days.

"She must be sick," she insisted, seeing the child a little out of sorts. She had one doctor in to look at her and then another, but they both agreed: "The little princess has nothing wrong with her, your majesty." Yet, as mothers will, Chryssa still felt uneasy.

"Then let this gipsy woman have a look at her," the king suggested. They led the ugly creature into the child's room, where Chryssa was standing by the bed.

When the fake healer saw her there in the freshness of her beauty, the blood rose to her head and she almost fainted from her jealousy. 'You won't escape me this time,' she assured herself. Putting on an air of deep concern, she enquired about the child's symptoms, pretended to examine her and then turned round to Chryssa.

"Your little girl is very ill," she said. "But don't worry, my lovely. She will get well again if you take these pomegranate leaves. Boil them to release their juice, then drink it hot."

"Why me?" asked Chryssa in surprise.

"Your majesty, the child's condition is grave and you must do exactly as I tell you. Once you have swallowed the potion, eat nothing afterwards. When evening comes, you will go down to the garden. Find an open glade bathed in the moonlight and throw these two pomegranate seeds before you. Then stamp them into the soil, one with your left foot and the other with your right. Be very careful to do everything exactly as I say. Next, bare your breasts and let the moonlight fall upon them. Stand without moving till you have counted up to forty, then go into the nursery and give the child your milk. Follow my instructions to the letter and you will have no further need of me. Ignore them and great harm may come, not only to your daughter but to the king and your fair self."

These words said, she turned to leave the nursery,

casting a sidelong look at Chryssa as she went. There was something in those eyes which sent a cold chill down the young queen's spine, for it brought back memories of her wicked stepmother.

'But this is no time for such thoughts,' she told herself. 'All that matters is to see my daughter well again.' And so she decided to follow the gipsy's instructions faithfully. She boiled the leaves and swallowed the bitter medicine they made, went down to the garden when night fell and there, by the light of the moon, threw the two pomegranate seeds to the ground and trod them in. But that was as far as she got, for suddenly she found herself unable to move her legs. They had taken root in the earth! In an instant, her hair turned to green leaves and Chryssa was transformed into a pomegranate tree. All she had time to see before her eyesight faded was the ugly face of the gipsy woman staring at her from behind a bush with a cruel smile upon her lips, the very same smile

her stepmother had worn when she first revealed her wicked nature.

Now if you think, dear reader, that the gipsy woman's task was done, then you are mistaken. All the next day and the one that followed, she hobbled round the garden on her stick. And you will see she had her reasons.

Meanwhile, the king soon realised that Chryssa had disappeared once more. He was out of his mind with worry and hunted high and low, but the queen was nowhere to be found. The next day, everyone in the palace took up the search, including the gardener. He soon spotted the gipsy woman and went across to her.

"What is all the fuss about?" she asked him. "Everyone seems very upset."

"We've lost the queen," the gardener replied. "She's disappeared, and we're all worried out of our minds. What a treasure she was, what a kind heart she had!

And how beautiful! In all my life I've never seen a lovelier creature."

The gipsy woman made a sour face when she heard her rival's beauty praised so highly, but she forced herself to say:

"Yes, she was quite pretty, I suppose. Let's look for her together, shall we? Have you been that way?"

"No," said the gardener, "but I'm going to search this place from end to end in any case, so we might as well begin where you suggest."

So they set off – and where did the gipsy woman take him but to the pomegranate tree?

"Hmm," said the gardener, scratching his head, "How did that tree spring up here so suddenly?"

"Why so surprised?" the gipsy asked him. "You speak as though you had never seen the tree before."

"But I water the whole garden every day, and there was never any pomegranate tree in this spot. I must be going out of my mind!" the gardener exclaimed.

"Perhaps you simply didn't notice it," said the gipsy woman innocently.

"Don't be ridiculous!" he retorted. "I know every blade of grass in this garden. Are you trying to tell me I missed a whole tree that takes years to grow? No, strange things are going on round here, things I can't explain. Yesterday the queen disappears – that's one mystery. And today I find a whole great pomegranate tree sprung up out of nowhere – and that's another mystery, if ever there was."

"Are you trying to tell the tree just grew by magic?" asked the gipsy, putting on her innocent look again.

"Well, can you explain it any other way?"

"Let me tell you one thing" she replied, "if that tree wasn't here a day or two ago, you can be quite sure that someone's casting magic spells on you. Now if you want to break those spells – and remember that you told me the queen has disappeared mysteriously, too – then there's only one way that'll work: Cut down the tree and burn it."

"Good for you!" the gardener cried. "That's exactly what I'll do – cut it down and burn it in my fireplace, and the sooner the better. I'll just go and get my axe."

He ran off and was back in a moment with a long axe in his hand. A few well-aimed strokes and the tree crashed to the ground.

Delighted that her wicked plan had worked so easily, the gipsy left the gardener to his work and limped up to the palace. The child had been handed over to her care. Not that there was really anything wrong with the little girl, of course, but the king feared for her health and the fake healer had persuaded him she needed careful nursing. Now that the queen had disappeared, the gipsy woman's services were needed, and they had set a bed up for her in the nursery. Nor was she in any hurry to leave.

She wanted to be sure that the tree really did go into the fire, and Chryssa burned to ashes. Once that happened, there would be no woman in the world to rival her in beauty. Though she might be a hideous sight at present, a fat-nosed gipsy woman with bald patches on her head and a clumsy limp, she would soon recover from her injuries and once again become the lovely queen that she had been before. Soon the time would come when she could once more look into her mirror and be told that no woman on this earth was lovelier than she.

But let us leave the evil stepmother snoring in her bed – in the hope that she never wakes up from her wicked dreams, the monster! – and go to see what had become of the pomegranate tree which was once the lovely Chryssa.

After the gardener had trimmed off all the smaller branches, he dragged the tree trunk back to his cottage to chop it into logs the right size for his fireplace. 'Maybe burning them will break the spells, just like the gipsy said. And who knows, perhaps the queen will come back to us then,' the good man told himself. He picked up his axe and took a good swing at the trunk. But the moment the blade struck home, he heard a voice cry out: "Oh! My leg!" He looked around him but there was no one to be seen. "Hm, I must have been imagining things again," he muttered, and took a second swing.

"Oh no! My hand!" came the same voice again.

"What's going on here? Don't say the tree is talking!" he exclaimed. "Whoever heard of such a thing? But let's be careful how I cut it, just the same." So this time he struck the trunk a lighter blow, and the voice cried out: "Oh, my finger!" The gardener was too kind-hearted to go on torturing the tree, so dropping his axe he opened his clasp knife and began to peel away the bark as gently as he could. To his amazement, first an arm appeared and then a leg, until eventually he had stripped the whole tree of its bark, revealing the form of a young woman. And surprise of surprises, who should it be but Chryssa, the lost queen! The gardener was overjoyed. "The queen is found!" he cried. "The queen is found!" jumping up and down in his excitement.

"Sshh!" warned Chryssa, climbing out of her prison-in the tree trunk. "If the gipsy woman hears you, we'll both be done for!"

"Not the one with the swollen nose?" gasped the gardener.

"Yes, she's the one who did it. When I was shut inside the pomegranate tree I heard her telling you to burn me — but how could I speak, encased from head to foot in wood? Go and find the king now — but you mustn't say a word of any of this. Think of some way to bring him here, and while you're away I'll prepare some food for you to offer him."

"Persuade the king to come to my poor cottage?

That may not be as easy as you think, your majesty," the gardener said doubtfully.

"Easy compared to saving a queen's life," smiled Chryssa. "You've already done me that great service, so surely you can accomplish the little that remains! But remember, nobody must see you, and you mustn't let a single word of this slip past your lips, in case the gipsy hears I'm still alive."

The gardener reluctantly went off to do as Chryssa told him. He paced up and down outside the palace gate, but did not have the courage to go in. But eventually he saw the king coming down to the garden and this gave him the excuse he needed for approaching. He began to ask his master what he should plant in the places where the trees had died, leading him by a route which would take them past the cottage.

"Your majesty," he said when they arrived, "I hope you won't think it's forward of me, but as this is the

first time you have visited my humble home, would you do me the honour of allowing me to offer you a little something?"

The king accepted graciously, so the gardener brought out a little table and a chair, then returned with a plate on which there stood a slice of cherry pie. While the gardener went in again to fetch a glass of water, the king picked up the pie and took a bite. His teeth hit something hard. Pulling it out, he saw it was not the cherry stone he had expected, but a ring! His heart leapt in his breast, for it was Chryssa's! By now the gardener had come out with the water.

"Tell me, my man, who made this cherry pie?" the king demanded.

"Er, it's, um, a poor girl I took in, your majesty." Then, gaining confidence: "She's almost like a daughter to me. Come out and meet the king, my dear!"

When Chryssa came out, the king jumped to his feet. She fell into his arms and they hugged each

other long and hard, tears streaming down their faces.

"How did you disappear?" the young king asked his wife at last.

So she told him all about the limping gipsy woman with the swollen nose, and how she was neither a gipsy nor a healer, but the wicked stepmother who had sworn to do away with her. She told him how she had been turned into a pomegranate tree and would have burned to ashes had it not been for the gardener.

At first the king stood open-mouthed in wonder, but his lips drew into a thin, hard line as Chryssa's tale unfolded. The witch's days of casting spells were ended. He would put a stop to her evil ambitions, magic or no magic! Dashing up to the nursery, he found their little daughter crying fit to break her heart and the gipsy woman sunk in snoring sleep, as if nothing were amiss. Calling for his guards, he gave his orders: "Do away with her!" And so they dragged her off just as she lay, mattress, pillows and all, not even forgetting her walking stick and the bag of magic potions. Who knew, she might have need of them where she was going! They carried her up to the highest tower of the palace and cast her into the deep gorge below, where she was smashed into a thousand pieces.

Then the king went down again into the garden and brought queen Chryssa to the palace. She folded the child in her arms and it waved its little hands in pleasure. Now the bad times were truly ended, and the happiness which reigned in the palace was even greater than before. In the course of time the royal couple were blessed with other children, and life was one long round of joyous celebrations. The gardener was always an honoured guest at these festivities and so were Chryssa's brothers, brought home from their wanderings in distant lands. The good old cook was invited, too, to let her know she was forgiven for all the trouble she had so innocently started, while as for the kind old lady from the castle with the forty chambers, she never had to live alone again. But when it was a very special occasion, they never forgot me, the wandering minstrel who has told you this strange story. They loved me to entertain them with my tales and my lute, and the king always showed me special favour. Why, would you believe it, he would even select the choicest dish before him and command that it be taken over to me. That shows you how much his majesty loved my stories!

And if you don't believe me, I can't say that I blame you.

Not all that you read in such tales is true.
What you believe is up to you!

The Ballad of the Dead Brother

A mother boasted nine brave sons and one dear daughter, Virtue,
Who was the apple of her eye, and loved by all around her.
For twelve long years she kept her hid; she never saw the sunlight.
Her mother bathed her in the night, beneath the moon
she combed her.
By starlight and before the dawn she wove her golden tresses.

Suitors arrived from Babylon, to seek her hand in marriage.
Eight of her brothers were against, all but young Constantinos.
"Mother, let Virtue go," he said, "to be a bride in Asia,

185

For I, too, travel far from home and go to distant places
And if we are together there, we shall not feel like strangers."
"You are a good lad," she replied, "and yet you argue badly;
For what if I should die, my son, and what if sickness strikes me?
Should bad luck chance, good fortune come, who will go
and bring her?"

"I appoint the heavens as my judge and call the saints to witness:
If death should strike or sickness come, bad luck or good fortune,
Alive or dead, I promise this: I will bring her to you."

Her daughter Virtue was led away, and in Babylon was married.
Then evil days befell them all, a time of loss and grieving.
Death came upon them in the night, and took off all nine brothers,
Leaving their mother all alone, a broken reed, defenceless.
She wept hot tears at her cruel fate, bewailed the blows it dealt her.
By her son's grave she tore her hair and cursed him for his rashness:
"A curse upon you, Constantine, a thousand curses on you
For letting Virtue leave her home and go off into exile!

The Ballade of the Dead Brother

You made a solemn oath to me. When will you keep your promise?
You called on Heaven to be your judge, named the saints as witness
That should death strike or illness come, you would bring her to me
Alive or dead, you swore an oath: that you would bring my Virtue."

With the force of her bitter curse, the cry of a wounded mother,
The grave split open at her feet; Constantine rose before her!
He made of the clouds a flying steed, wove its reins
from the starlight
And called on the moon to go with him, to bring back
Virtue to her.

He left the mountains in his wake, he leapt the hills before him
And found her brushing out her hair, by Babylon's cool waters.
He gestured to her from afar, and drawing nearer told her:
"Come, sister dear, let us away, and go to find our mother."
"What brings you to me in such haste? Tell me straight,
dear brother.
Is it good tidings that you bring, and should I wear my jewels?

187

Or do you bring unhappy news, that I should wear my mourning?"
"Come, sister dear, come home with me, no matter what
you're wearing!"

The horse went down upon its knees; he pulled her up behind him.
Beside the road they galloped down, little birds were singing.
They did not sing as birds are wont, nor twittered
they like swallows,
Their song was like the speech of men, and this is what
it told them:
"Whoever saw such a lovely maid, behind a dead man riding!"

"Listen, dear brother!" Virtue cried, "Hear what the birds
are saying!"
"They are only sparrows," he replied, "let them sing what
they wish to."
But down the road they met other birds, who cried out
in their horror:
"It goes against nature to see the dead keep company

with the living!"

"Ah, Constantine! Hear what they say, hear what
the birds are singing:
They see a dead man riding by, in company with the living!"
"It is spring," he replied, "birds always sing in May when
they are nesting."

"I fear you, brother!" the girl cried out. "Why do you smell
of incense?"
" Last night we went to pray at St John's, and the air was
heavy with it."
But as they rode on down the road, other birds called to them:
"See what wonders there are in the world: a corpse riding by
with a beauty!"

Once again Virtue caught their words; it broke her heart
to hear them.
"Oh Constantine, brother, do you know what

the little birds are saying?"
"Leave them to twitter, Virtue dear, let them get on
with their chirping."

"Why have your good looks faded so, the manly strength
that you boasted?"
"Why is your golden hair all gone, the handsome moustache
you sported?"
"I lost them all when I fell ill, a long time ago, dear sister."

They reached the church, he spurred his horse
and disappeared beneath her,
With a thunder-clap his tomb gaped wide, and swallowed him
for ever.

Virtue turned and walked on alone, to the house
she had been born in.
She saw the garden dry and bare, trees with their leaves
all withered,

190

The Ballade of the Dead Brother

The pot plants dead, the herbs dried up, tall weeds
in the pathway,
The front door closed, no keys to be found,
shutters fast on the windows.
She knocked until the windows shook, and at last
a weak voice answered:
"If you be a friend then come on in, but if an enemy, leave me.
And if you are Charon, king of the dead, I've no more children
to give you
For Virtue, the one I loved above all, is away in a distant country."

"Get up, mother dear and open the door! Get up sweet mother,
I beg you!"
"Who can it be that knocks at my door? Who is it calls me mother?"
"Open, dear mother, open and see! It is I, your daughter Virtue!"
She ran down the stairs, fell into her arms,
and both died upon the instant.

171
1.40
6840
171
239.40